500

FREE
DAYS OUT
in Britain & Ireland

This edition published 2007
© Automobile Association Developments
Limited 2007

The Automobile Association Development
Limited retains the copyright in the current
edition © 2007 and in all subsequent
editions, reprints and amendments to
editions.

A CIP catalogue record for this book is
available from the British Library.

Directory generated by the AA Establishment
Database, Information Research.

Cover photo: AA/M Jourdan
All images in this guide are held in the
Association's own photo library (AA World
Travel Library) and were taken by the
following photographers: 1 AA/C Sawyer;
3 AA/L Whitwam; 5 AA/N Setchfield
Typeset by Jamie Wiltshire
Printed in Italy by G.Canale & C.S.p.A.

Published by AA Publishing, which is a
trading name of Automobile Association
Developments Limited, whose registered
office is Fanum House, Basing View,
Basingstoke, Hampshire RG21 4EA.
Registered number 1878835.
ISBN 10: 0-7495-5315-4
ISBN 13: 978-0-7495-5315-9

A03198

Welcome to the Guide

The AA's 500 Free Days Out provides information on a comprehensive selection of attractions in England, Scotland, Wales and Ireland, all free of admission charges. These range through factory tours, standing stones, castles, parks and gardens to town, city and national museums and art galleries. Through these pages, you can discover many of the country's most beautiful open spaces, ancient monuments, evocations of our cultural, industrial and social heritage and some of our finest collections of art. The entries give a short description for each attraction, along with contact details, opening times, how to get there, and specfic facilities for parking, refreshments and accessibility.

Contents

England	7
Channel Islands	142
Isle of Man	144
Scotland	145
Wales	203
Northern Ireland	224
Republic of Ireland	249

How to use this Guide

① LA GREVE DE LECQ

Greve de Lecq Barracks

St Mary

② ☎ 01534 483193 & 482238

🖻 01534 485873

e-mail: enquiries@nationaltrustjersey.org.je

Web: www.nationaltrustjersey.org.je

③ Dir: *on side of valley, overlooking beach*

Originally serving as an outpost of the British Empire, these barracks, built in 1810, were used for civilian housing from the end of WWI to 1972, when they were bought by the National Trust and made into a museum that depicts the life of soldiers who were stationed here in the 19th century. Also includes a collection of old horse-drawn carriages.

④ Times: *Open: 4 Jun-25 Sept, Sun only.

⑤ Facilities: ℗ (100yds) ♿ (wheelchair ramps), toilets for disabled (located in ground floor toilets), shop ⊗ (ex assist dogs)

① The Directory is arranged in countries, counties, then in alphabetical order by location within each county. County names appear down the side of each page.

② Telephone numbers have the STD code shown before the telephone number. (If dialling Northern Ireland from England, Scotland or Wales, use STD code, but for the Republic of Ireland you need to prefix the number with 00353, and drop the first zero from the irish area code).

③ Directions may be given after the address of each attraction and where shown have been provided by the places of interest themselves. Please telephone for directions where these are not supplied.

4 Opening times quoted in the guide are inclusive – for instance, where it says Apr-Oct, that place will be open from the beginning of April to the end of October.

5 Facilities This section includes information on parking, refreshments, accessibility and whether dogs are allowed admission. Visitors with mobility disabilities should look for the wheelchair symbol showing where all or most of the attraction is accessible to wheelchair users. We stongly recommend that you telephone in advance of your visit to check the exact details, particularly regarding access to toilets and refreshments facilities. Assistance dogs are usually accepted where the attractions show the 'No Dogs' symbol unless otherwise stated.

See page 6 for a key to the symbols and abbreviations used in this guide.
Please note opening times and free admission policies are subject to change. There may be charges made for parking, toilets or audio equipment etc.
Please check with the attraction before making your journey.

Key to symbols and abbreviations

☎ Telephone number

▤ Fax

🅿 Parking at establishments

Ⓟ Parking nearby

☕ Café / refreshments

🍽 Restaurant

🪑 Picnic area

♿ Suitable for visitors in wheelchairs (plus further information for disabled visitors)

🚫 No dogs

🚌 Info on coaches

▤ Worksheets available

* Opening dates/times do not relate to 2007. These should be used only as a guide. Please telephone attraction to confirm current information.

✛ Cadw (Welsh Historic Monuments)

✜ English Heritage

❧ National Trust

❦ National Trust for Scotland

▉ Historic Scotland

BH Bank Holidays

PH Public Holidays

Etr Easter

ex except

AMPTHILL
Houghton House

Web: www.english-heritage.org.uk

Dir: *1m NE off A421*

Now a ruin, the mansion was built for Mary Countess of Pembroke, the sister of Sir Philip Sidney. Inigo Jones is thought to have been involved in work on the house, which may have been the original 'House Beautiful' in Bunyan's Pilgrim's Progress.

Times: Open at all reasonable times.

Facilities: ♿ & 🚌 ⛲

BEDFORD
Bedford Museum

Castle Lane, MK40 3XD

☎ 01234 353323

🖷 01234 273401

e-mail: bmuseum@bedford.gov.uk

Web: www.bedfordmuseum.org

Dir: *close to town bridge and Embankment*

Embark on a fascinating journey through the history of north Bedfordshire. Go back in time and visit the rural room sets and the Old School Museum, where Blackbeard's Sword, 'Old Billy' the longest-living horse, and other curiosities can be found. Housed in the former Higgins and Sons Brewery, the museum is situated within the gardens of what was once Bedford Castle.

Times: *Open all year, Tue-Sat 11-5, Sun 2-5. (Closed Mon ex BH Mon afternoon, Good Fri & Xmas).

Facilities: ℗ (50yds) 🖵 🪑 & (lift available on request, subject to staff availability), toilets for disabled, shop ⊗ (ex assist dogs) 🚌

BEDFORDSHIRE

BEDFORDSHIRE

BEDFORD
Cecil Higgins Art Gallery
Castle Lane, MK40 3RP
☎ 01234 211222
🖹 01234 327149
e-mail: chag@bedford.gov.uk
Web: www.cecilhigginsartgallery.org
Dir: *in town centre close to Embankment*
A recreated Victorian mansion, arranged as though the house is still lived in. Includes furniture designed by architect William Burges. Outstanding ceramics, glass and changing exhibition of prints, drawings and watercolours. Also Thomas Lester lace collection.
Times: *Open all year, Tue-Sat 11-5, Sun & BH Mon 2-5. (Closed Mon, Good Fri, 25-26 Dec & 1 Jan).
Facilities: ℗ (100yds) (pay & display) (free on Sun) ⊑ ⊼ ৬ (wheelchair available), toilets for disabled (extra large cubicle, pull cord), shop, tours available ⊗ (ex assist dogs) 🚌 (advance booking, max 50 people)

LUTON
Wardown Park Museum
Wardown Park, Old Bedford Road, LU2 7HA
☎ 01582 546722 & 546739
🖹 01582 546763
e-mail: museum.gallery@luton.gov.uk
Web: www.luton.gov.uk/museums
Dir: *Follow brown signs from the town centre north. Turn off A6 towards Bedford*
A Victorian mansion, with displays illustrating the natural and cultural history, archaeology and industries of the area, including the development of Luton's hat industry, and the Bedfordshire and Hertfordshire Regimental Collections. New 'Luton Life' displays tell the story of the town and its residents over the past 200 years. Exhibitions and events throughout the year.
Times: *Open all year, Tue-Sat 10-5, Sun 1-5. (Closed Xmas, 1 Jan & Mon ex BH Mons).
Facilities: ❶ ℗ (500yds) ⊑ ⊼ ৬ (parking adjacent to entrance, lift to 1st floor), toilets for disabled, shop ⊗ (ex assist dogs) 🚌 (advance bookings only)

LUTON

Stockwood Park Museum

Stockwood Country Park, Farley Hill, LU1 4BH

☎ 01582 738714 & 546739

🖹 01582 546763

e-mail: museum.gallery@luton.gov.uk

Web: www.luton.gov.uk/museums

Dir: *signposted from M1 junct 10 and from Hitchin, Dunstable, Bedford and town centre*

The museum is set in period gardens which incorporate the Ian Hamilton Finlay Sculpture Gardens. The Mossman collection of horse-drawn vehicles traces the history of transport from Roman times. Craft demonstrations in summer. Telephone for details of events.

Times: *Open all year; Mar-Oct, Tue-Sun 10-5; Nov-Mar, wknds 10-4. (Closed Xmas & 1 Jan)

Facilities: ❷ ℗ (200yds) (coach parking by appointment) ➤ ⛱ ♿ (stair lift, parking, induction loop, automatic door), toilets for disabled, shop, audio commentaries available ⊗ (ex assist dogs) 🚌 (advance bookings)

LUTON

John Dony Field Centre

Hancock Drive, Bushmead, LU2 7SF

☎ 01582 486983

e-mail: donyj@luton.gov.uk

Web: www.luton.gov.uk/museums

Dir: *signposted from rdbt on A6, at Barnfield College on New Bedford Rd*

This is a purpose built study centre for exploring the landscapes, plants and animals of the Luton area. Featuring permanent displays on local archaeology, natural history and the management of the local nature reserve, it explains how ancient grasslands and hedgerows are conserved and follows 4000 years of history from Bronze Age to modern times.

Times: *Open all year, Mon-Fri 9.30-4.45. Closed BHs.

Facilities: ❷ ℗ (100yds) ♿ toilets for disabled ⊗ (ex assist dogs) 🚌 (prior booking required)

BEDFORDSHIRE

BERKSHIRE

NEWBURY
West Berkshire Museum

The Wharf, RG14 5AS

☎ 01635 30511

🖺 01635 38535

e-mail: museum@westberks.gov.uk

Web: westberkshiremuseum.org.uk

Dir: *from London take M4 junct 13, then southbound on A34, follow signs for town centre*

Occupying two adjoining buildings in the centre of Newbury; the Cloth Hall built in 1627 and the Granary built in 1720. The museum includes displays of fine and decorative art, costume, local history and archaeology.

Times: Open all year Tue-Sat 10-5. Open BH Feb-Nov .

Facilities: ℗ (15yds) ♿, shop ⊗ (ex assist dogs) 🚌 (advance booking, max 50)

READING
Museum of English Rural Life

University of Reading, Redlands Road, RG1 5EX

☎ 0118 378 8660

🖺 0118 378 5632

e-mail: merl@reading.ac.uk

Web: www.merl.org.uk

Dir: *close to the Royal Berkshire Hospital*

Recently moved to larger premises, this museum houses a national collection of agricultural, domestic and crafts exhibits used in the English countryside over the last 150 years. Special facilities are available for school parties. The museum also contains extensive documentary and photographic archives, which can be studied by appointment. There is a regular programme of events and activities, please see website for details.

Times: *Open all year, Tue-Fri, 10-4.30, Sat & Sun 2-4.30 (Closed BHs & Xmas-New Year).

Facilities: ℗ ♿ (Chair lifts, hearing loop) toilets for disabled, shop ⊗ (ex assist dogs) 🚌

WINDSOR

Household Cavalry Museum

Combermere Barracks, St Leonards Road, SL4 3DN

☎ 01753 755112

🖹 01753 755161

Dir: *on St Leonards Rd opposite King Edward VII Hospital*

One of the finest military museums in Britain, with comprehensive displays of the uniforms, weapons, horse furniture (tack, regalia, etc) and armour used by the Household Cavalry from 1600 to the present day.

Times: *Open all year Mon-Fri (ex BH) 9-12.30 & 2-4.30. **Facilities:** ⅍ shop ⊗ 🚌

BRISTOL

Bristol's Blaise Castle House Museum

Henbury Road, Henbury, BS10 7QS

☎ 0117 903 9818

e-mail: general_museum@bristol-city.gov.uk

Web: www.bristol-city.gov.uk/museums

Dir: *4m NW of city, off B4057*

Built in the 18th century for a Quaker banker, this mansion is now Bristol's Museum of Social History. Nearby Blaise Hamlet is a picturesque estate village, designed by John Nash.

Times: Open all year, Sat-Wed 10-5. (Closed 25-26 Dec).

Facilities: 🅿 ℗ (200yds) 🍴 ⅍ shop, tours available ⊗ (ex assist dogs) 🚌 (pre-booking)

BERKSHIRE/BRISTOL

BRISTOL

BRISTOL
Bristol's Red Lodge
Park Row, BS1 5LJ
☎ 0117 921 1360
e-mail: general_museum@bristol-city.gov.uk
Web: www.bristol-city.gov.uk/museums
Dir: *5 mins walk from city centre*
The house was built in 1590 and then altered in 1730. It has fine oak panelling and carved stone chimney pieces and is furnished in the style of both periods. The garden has now been laid out in Elizabethan style.
Times: Open all year Sat-Wed 10-5. (Closed 25-26 Dec).
Facilities: ℗ (Adjacent) tours available ⊗ (ex assist dogs) 🚌 (pre-booking)

BRISTOL
Bristol's City Museum & Art Gallery
Queen's Road, Clifton, BS8 1RL
☎ 0117 922 3571
🖷 0117 922 2047
e-mail: general_museum@bristol-city.gov.uk
Web: www.bristol-city.gov.uk/museums
Dir: *follow signs to city centre, then follow tourist board signs to City Museum & Art Gallery*
Regional and international collections representing ancient history, natural sciences, and fine and applied arts. Displays include dinosaurs, Bristol ceramics, silver, Chinese and Japanese ceramics. A full programme of Special Exhibitions take place throughout the year. Ring for details.
Times: Open all year, daily 10-5. (Closed 25-26 Dec).
Facilities: ℗ (400yds) ⊋ (licensed) ♿ (lift) toilets for disabled, shop, tours available ⊗ (ex assist dogs) 🚌 (pre-booking)

BRISTOL
Bristol's Georgian House

7 Great George St, off Park Street, BS1 5RR

☎ 0117 921 1362

🖹 0117 922 2047

e-mail: general_museum@bristol-city.gov.uk

Web: www.bristol-city.gov.uk/museums

Dir: *5 mins walk from city centre*

A carefully preserved example of a late 18th-century merchant's town house, with many original features and furnished to illustrate life both above and below stairs. A bedroom is now open, featuring a four-poster bed plus a small display recounting Bristol's involvement in the slave trade.

Times: Open all year Sat-Wed, 10-5. (Closed 25-26 Dec).

Facilities: ⓟ (pay & display street parking) tours available ⊗ (ex assist dogs) 🚌 (pre-booking)

BRISTOL
Arnolfini

16 Narrow Quay, BS1 4QA

☎ 0117 917 2300 & 0117 917 2301

🖹 0117 917 2303

e-mail: boxoffice@arnolfini.org.uk

Web: www.arnolfini.org.uk

Dir: *From M32 follow brown signs*

Located in a 19th-century warehouse in Bristol's harbourside, Arnolfini is one of Europe's leading centres for contemporary arts. The internationally acclaimed programme includes visual arts exhibitions, live art, performance, dance, cinema and talks and lectures.

Times: Open all year, daily 10-8. (Thu, galleries close at 6).

Facilities: ⓟ (100yds) (Disabled parking on site) ⊑ ⦿ (licensed) 🛏 ♿ toilets for disabled (on every floor), shop, tours available ⊗ (ex assist dogs) 🚌 (pre-book by phone)

BRISTOL

HIGH WYCOMBE
Wycombe Museum

Castle Hill House, Priory Avenue, HP13 6PX

☎ 01494 421895

🖷 01494 421897

e-mail: museum@wycombe.gov.uk

Web: www.wycombe.gov.uk/museum

Dir: *signposted by brown tourist sign from A404 (Amersham Hill) N of High Wycombe town centre just past railway station*

High Wycombe is famous for chair making and the museum has an extensive collection of chairs and artefacts from the furniture industry. There is also a gallery featuring local scenes and artists.

Times: *Open all year, Mon-Sat 10-5, Sun 2-5. Closed on BHs except special events - ring for details.

Facilities: 🅿 🅟 (on road outside) ☖ ㅋ ♿ (portable induction loop, special parking & drop off point), toilets for disabled, shop, audio commentaries available ⊗ (ex assist dogs) 🚌 (pre-booking)

CAMBRIDGE
Fitzwilliam Museum

Trumpington Street, CB2 1RB

☎ 01223 332900

🖷 01223 332923

e-mail: fitzmuseum-enquiries@lists.cam.ac.uk

Web: www.fitzmuseum.cam.ac.uk

Dir: *M11 junct 11, 12 or 13. Near city centre*

The Fitzwilliam is the art museum of the University of Cambridge and one of the oldest public museums in Britain. Has magnificent collections spanning several centuries and civilisations, including antiquities from Ancient Egypt, Greece and Rome.

Times: Open all year Tue-Sat 10-5, Sun 12-5. (Closed Mon ex BH, & 24-26, 31 Dec & 1 Jan).

Facilities: 🅟 (400yds) (2hr max, metered) ☖ (licensed) ㅋ ♿ (induction loop), toilets for disabled, shop, tours available audio, commentaries available ⊗ (ex assist dogs) 🚌 (pre-book)

CAMBRIDGE
University Museum of Archaeology & Anthropology

Downing Street, CB2 3DZ

☎ 01223 333516

🖹 01223 333517

e-mail: cumaa@hermes.cam.ac.uk

Web: http://museum.archanth.cam.ac.uk

Dir: *located opposite Crowne Plaza Hotel in city centre*

The museum was established in 1884. Some of the highlights are Pacific material collected on Captain Cook's voyages of exploration and a 46-foot high totem pole from Canada. See local, national and world archaeological finds in the Archaeology Galleries, including painted pottery from Peru, gilded Anglo-Saxon brooches, and Roman altar stones.

Times: *Open all year Tue-Sat 2-4.30. (Closed 1wk Etr & 1wk Xmas). Telephone for extended summer hours.

Facilities: ℗ (100yds) ♿ (lift available), shop ⊗ (ex assist dogs) 🚌 (pre-booking essential)

CAMBRIDGE
Scott Polar Research Institute Museum

Lensfield Road, CB2 1ER

☎ 01223 336540

🖹 01223 336549

e-mail: enquiries@spri.cam.ac.uk

Web: www.spri.cam.ac.uk

Dir: *1km S of city centre*

An international centre for polar studies, including a museum featuring displays of Arctic and Antarctic expeditions, with special emphasis on those of Captain Scott and the exploration of the Northwest Passage. Other exhibits include Inuit work and other arts of the polar regions, as well as displays on current scientific exploration. Public lectures run from October to December and February to April.

Times: *Open all year, Tue-Sat 2.30-4. Closed some BHs wknds, public & university hols.

Facilities: ℗ (400yds) ♿ shop ⊗ (ex assist dogs) 🚌 (pre-booking essential)

CAMBRIDGESHIRE

CAMBRIDGESHIRE/CHESHIRE

RAMSEY
Ramsey Abbey Gatehouse

Abbey School, Huntingdon, PE17 1DH

☎ 0870 609 5388

🖹 01263 734924

Web: www.nationaltrust.org.uk/regions/eastanglia

Dir: *SE edge of Ramsey, where Chatteris Road joins B1096*

The ruins of this 15th-century gatehouse, together with the 13th-century Lady Chapel, are all that remain of the abbey. Half of the gatehouse was taken away after the Dissolution. Built in ornate late-Gothic style, it has panelled buttresses and friezes.

Times: *Open Apr-Oct, daily 10-5.

Facilities: ⊗ 🚌 �である

CHESTER
Chester Visitor Centre

Vicars Lane, CH1 1QX

☎ 01244 351609

🖹 01244 403188

e-mail: tis@chestercc.gov.uk

Web: www.chestertourism.com

Dir: *opposite St Johns Church Roman Amphitheatre on Vicars Lane.*

Among the attractions are guided walks of Chester; World of Names, which explores the history of family and first names; displays on the history of Chester; a café and a gift shop. Chester is the most complete walled city in Britain, and was originally settled by the Romans in the first century AD. The city also played its part in battles with the Vikings, the Norman Invasion, and the Civil War.

Times: *Open all year, Mon-Sat 10-5, Sun 10-4

Facilities: Ⓟ (200yds) (short stay) 🖵 🎋 ♿ (ramped access from Vicars Lane), toilets for disabled, shop 🚌

FOWEY
St Catherine's Castle

Web: www.english-heritage.org.uk

Dir: *0.75m SW of Fowey along footpath off A3082*

A small sixteenth-century fort built by Henry VIII to defend Fowey Harbour. It has two storeys with gun ports at ground level.

Times: Open at any reasonable time.

Facilities: ℗ (0.5m) ⊗ (ex on leads) 🚌 ⊞

SANCREED
Carn Euny Ancient Village

Web: www.english-heritage.org.uk

Dir: *1.25m SW of Sancreed, off A30*

The remains of an Iron-Age settlement. Surviving features include the foundations of stone huts and an intriguing curved underground passage or 'fogou'.

Times: Open at any reasonable time.

Facilities: ℗ (600yds) 🚌 ⊞

CORNWALL

CORNWALL/CUMBRIA

TRURO
Royal Cornwall Museum
River Street, TR1 2SJ
☎ 01872 272205
🖹 01872 240514
e-mail: enquiries@royalcornwallmuseum.org.uk
Web: www.royalcornwallmuseum.org.uk
Dir: *follow A390 towards town centre*
Cornwall's oldest and most prestigious museum, famed for its internationally important collections. See large collections of minerals, an unwrapped mummy, and many aspects of Cornwall's unique culture. The art gallery has a fine collection of Newlyn School paintings, while the museum has a range of exhibitions throughout the year together with an extensive programme for all the family. Contact the museum for details of events and activities.
Times: Open all year, Mon-Sat 10-5. Library closes 1-2, 10-1 Sat. (Closed BHs & Sun).
Facilities: ℗ (200yds) (disabled parking on street) ⊑ ⦿ (licensed) ﹠ (lift, ramps to main entrances), toilets for disabled, shop ⊗ (ex assist dogs) 🚌

BARROW-IN-FURNESS
The Dock Museum
North Road, LA14 2PW
☎ 01229 894444
🖹 01229 811361
e-mail: dockmuseum@barrowbc.gov.uk
Web: www.dockmuseum.org.uk
Dir: *A590 to Barrow-in-Furness. Follow brown tourist signs*
Explore and relive the fascinating history of Barrow-in-Furness at this museum. Discover how the industrial revolution prompted the growth of the town from a small hamlet into a major industrial power through models, graphics and computer kiosks.
Times: *Open mid Apr-Nov (Tue-Fri 10-5, Sat-Sun 11-5); Nov-Mar (Wed-Fri 10.30-4, Sat-Sun 11-4.30)
Facilities: ℗ ℗ (200yds) designated disabled spaces ⊑ ⢍ ﹠ (hearing & induction loops, 2 w/chairs for loan) toilets for disabled, shop, tours available ⊗ (ex assist dogs) 🚌

BROUGH
Brough Castle

CA17 4EJ

☎ 0191 261 1585

Web: www.english-heritage.org.uk

Dir: *8m SE of Appleby, S of A66*

Dating from Roman times the 12th century keep at this site replaced an earlier stronghold destroyed by the Scots in 1174. It was restored by Lady Anne Clifford in the 17th century. You can still see the outline of her kitchen gardens.

Times: Open at any reasonable time.

Facilities: ℗ ⊗ (ex dogs on leads) 🚌 ♿

CARLISLE
The Guildhall Museum

Green Market, CA3 8JE

☎ 01228 534781

🖹 01228 810249

e-mail: enquiries@tulliehouse.co.uk

Web: www.tulliehouse.co.uk

Dir: *town centre, opposite The Crown & Mitre Hotel*

One of Carlisle's oldest buildings, c.1405 and Grade I listed. The Guildhall was once the meeting place of Carlisle's eight trade guilds, few of which still meet today. Experience the cabin-like atmosphere of the shoemaker's room and the 'modernised' butcher's room with its Victorian features. Amazing objects such as the medieval town chest, dating from 1400, two small silver balls (one dated 1599) - reputed to be the earliest surviving horse racing prizes in the country.

Times: *Open Apr-Oct, 12-4.30

Facilities: ℗ (500yds) (disc parking on street, 1 hr limit) shop ⊗ (ex assist dogs) 🚌 (no disabled access, steep stairs)

CUMBRIA

CUMBRIA

HARDKNOTT CASTLE ROMAN FORT
Hardknott Castle Roman Fort

Dir: *9m NE of Ravenglass, at W end of Hardknott Pass*

One of the most dramatic Roman sites in Britain, with stunning views of the Lakeland falls. The fort built between AD120 and AD138, controlled the road from Ravenglass to Ambleside. The remains include the headquarters building and Commandant's house, with a bath house and parade ground outside the fort.

Times: Open any reasonable time. Access may be hazardous in winter.

Facilities: ❷ Limited ⊗ (ex dogs on leads) ❧

KESWICK
Keswick Museum & Art Gallery

Fitz Park, Station Road, CA12 4NF

☎ 01768 773263

▤ 01768 780390

e-mail: keswick.museum@allerdale.gov.uk

Web: www.allerdale.gov.uk/keswick-museum

Dir: *M6 junct 40, A66 to Keswick. Follow Museum & Art Gallery tourist signs*

Keswick's surprising past, from industrial mining centre to peaceful tourist town, is revealed in this late Victorian museum. Set in the beautiful Fitz park, the collections cover local and natural history, famous inhabitants and visitors, including the Lake Poets. The art gallery hosts a variety of special exhibitions.

Times: Open Good Fri-Oct, Tue-Sat 10-4

Facilities: ❷ (on road outside) (2 hour limit) ▤ ♿ (ramp at front entrance, with handrails) shop ⊗ (ex guide and hearing dogs)

PENRITH

Wetheriggs Country Pottery

Clifton Dykes, CA10 2DH

☎ 01768 892733

📄 01768 892733 ext 231

e-mail: info@wetheriggs-pottery.co.uk

Web: www.wetheriggs-pottery.co.uk

Dir: *approx 2m off A6, S from Penrith, signed*

The only steam-powered pottery in Britain, with 7.5 acres of things to do, including the Pots of Fun Studio, where you can throw or paint a pot, Designer-Makers at work, Café and shops. Newt pond, play areas and pottery museum.

Times: *Open daily, Etr-Oct 10-5.30; Nov-Etr 10-4.30

Facilities: ❷ ☕ 🍴 (licensed) ♿ toilets for disabled, shop ⊗ (ex assist dogs) 🚌 (pre-booking essential)

SHAP

Shap Abbey

CA10 3NB

Dir: *1.5m W of Shap on bank of River Lowther*

Dedicated to St Mary Magdalene, the abbey was founded by the Premonstratensian order in 1199, but most of the ruins are of 13th-century date. The most impressive feature is the 16th-century west tower of the church.

Times: *Open at any reasonable time.

Facilities: ❷ ♿ ⊗ (ex dogs on leads) 🚌

CUMBRIA

DERBYSHIRE

DERBY

Derby Museum & Art Gallery

The Strand, DE1 1BS

☎ 01332 716659

🖹 01332 716670

e-mail: david.fraser@derby.gov.uk

Web: www.derby.gov.uk/museums

Dir: *follow directions to city centre*

The museum has a wide range of displays, notably of Derby porcelain, and paintings by the local artist Joseph Wright (1734-97). Also antiquities, natural history and militaria, as well as many temporary exhibitions.

Times: *Open all year, Mon 11-5, Tue-Sat 10-5, Sun & BHs 1-4. Closed Xmas & New Year, telephone for details.

Facilities: ℗ (50yds) ♿ (lift to all floors, portable mini-loop, large print labels), toilets for disabled (adapted W.C) shop, tours available, audio commentaries available ⊗ (ex assist dogs) 🚌

DERBY

The Silk Mill, Derby's Museum

Silk Mill Lane, off Full Street, DE1 3AR

☎ 01332 255308

🖹 01332 716670

e-mail: roger.shelley@derby.gov.uk

Web: www.derby.gov.uk/museums

Dir: *From Derby inner ring road, towards Cathedral & Assembly Rooms car park. 5 mins walk*

The museum is set in an early 18th-century silk mill and adjacent flour mill on the site of the world's first modern factory. Displays cover local mining, quarrying and industries, and include a collection of Rolls Royce aero-engines from 1915 to the present. Also a section on railway engineering in Derby.

Times: *Open all year, Mon 11-5, Tue-Sat 10-5, Sun & BHs 1-4. (Closed Xmas & New Year, telephone for details).

Facilities: ℗ 5 min walk (museum parking restricted to disabled) 🚻 ♿ (lift to all floors), toilets for disabled, shop tours available ⊗ (ex assist dogs) 🚌

DERBY

Pickford's House Museum of Georgian Life & Costume

41 Friar Gate, DE1 1DA

☎ 01332 255363

🖹 01332 255527

e-mail: elizabeth.spencer@derby.gov.uk

Web: www.derby.gov.uk/museums

Dir: *from A38 into Derby, follow signs to city centre*

The house was built in 1770 by the architect Joseph Pickford as a combined workplace and family home. It now shows domestic life at different periods. Other galleries are devoted to temporary exhibitions. Also a display on the growth of Georgian Derby.

Times: *Open all year, Mon 11-5, Tue-Sat 10-5, Sun & BHs 1-4. (Closed Xmas & New Year, telephone for details).

Facilities: ℗ ℗ (500yds) ♿ (tape guides, video with sign language subtitles), shop, tours available ⊗ (ex assist dogs) 🚌 (no parking facilities for coaches)

OLD WHITTINGTON

Revolution House

High Street, Chesterfield, S41 9JZ

☎ 01246 345727

🖹 01246 345720

e-mail: tourism@chesterfield.gov.uk

Web: www.visitchesterfield.info

Dir: *3m N of Chesterfield town centre, on B6052 off A61, signposted*

Originally the Cock and Pynot alehouse, this 17th-century cottage was the scene of a meeting between local noblemen to plan their part in the Revolution of 1688, a series of events that led to the overthrow of James II in favour of William and Mary of Orange. The house is now furnished in 17th-century style.

Times: *Open daily (ex Tue) 11-4 from 8 Apr-30 Sep. Xmas: 16-24 & 27-31 Dec from 11-4

Facilities: ℗ (100yds) ♿ (signing available by prior arrangement), shop, tours available ⊗ (ex assist dogs) 🚌 (by prior arrangement)

DERBYSHIRE

DERBYSHIRE/DEVON

BUCKFASTLEIGH
Buckfast Abbey
TQ11 0EE

☎ 01364 645500

📄 01364 643891

e-mail: enquiries@buckfast.org.uk

Web: www.buckfast.org

Dir: *0.5m from A38, midway between Exeter and Plymouth. Turn off at 'Dart Bridge' junct and follow brown tourist signs*

The Abbey, founded in 1018, was dissolved by Henry VIII in the 16th century. Restoration began in 1907, when four monks with little building experience began the work. The church was built on the old foundations, using local blue limestone and Ham Hill stone. The precinct contains several medieval buildings, including the 14th-century guest hall which shows the history of the Abbey.

Times: *Open all year daily. Closed Good Fri, 24-26 Dec.

Facilities: ❷ ☭ (licensed) 🪑 ♿ (Braille/audio information), toilets for disabled, shop ⊗ (ex assist dogs) 🚌

DARTMOUTH
Bayard's Cove Fort
TQ6 9AT

Web: www.english-heritage.org.uk

Dir: *in Dartmouth on riverfront*

Built by the townspeople to protect the harbour, the remains of the circular stronghold still stand at the southern end of the harbour.

Times: Open at any reasonable times.

Facilities: ⊗ 🚌 ⛩

EXETER
Guildhall
High Street, EX4 3EB

☎ 01392 665500

e-mail: guildhall@exeter.gov.uk

Web: www.exeter.gov.uk/visiting

Dir: *city centre*

This is one of the oldest municipal buildings still in use. It was built in 1330 and then altered in 1446, and the arches and façade were added in 1592-5. The roof timbers rest on bosses of bears holding staves, and there are portraits of Exeter dignitaries, guild crests, civic silver and regalia.

Times: Open when there are no mayoral functions. Times are posted outside weekly. Special opening by arrangement.

Facilities: ℗ (200yds) ♿ toilets for disabled, tours available ⊗ (ex assist dogs) 🚌

EXETER
Quay House Visitor Centre
46 The Quay, EX2 4AN

☎ 01392 271611

🖷 01392 265625

e-mail: quayhouse@exeter.gov.uk

Web: www.exeter.gov.uk/visiting

Two thousand years of Exeter history in an audio-visual presentation of the city from Roman times to present day. Learn about the city's quayside history from the small museum.

Times: Open all year, Apr-Oct, daily 10-5; Nov-Mar, Sat-Sun 11-4.

Facilities: ℗ (no parking on quayside), shop, audio commentaries available ⊗ (ex assist dogs) 🚌

DEVON

DEVON

LYDFORD

Lydford Castle and Saxon Town

EX20 4BH

Dir: *in Lydford off A386*

Standing above the gorge of the River Lyd, this tower, dating back to the 12th century, was notorious as a prison. The earthworks of the original Norman fort lie to the south.

Times: *Open at any reasonable times.

Facilities: ❷ 🚌 ♿

OTTERTON

Otterton Mill

Budleigh Salterton, EX9 7HG

☎ 01392 568521

e-mail: escape@ottertonmill.com

Web: www.ottertonmill.com

Dir: *on B3178 between Budleigh Salterton and Newton Poppleford*

Set beside the River Otter in one of Devon's loveliest valleys, Otterton Mill is a centuries-old working watermill, a famous bakery and shop full of local produce, a restaurant, and a gallery of arts and crafts from local artists. Please see website for details of music nights and art events.

Times: Open daily, 10-5.

Facilities: ❷ ℗ (100yds) ☕ ⫶◯⫶ (licensed) ♿ (free entry to ground floor), toilets for disabled, shop, tours available 🚌 (pre-booked)

PLYMOUTH

Plymouth City Museum & Art Gallery

Drake Circus, PL4 8AJ

☎ 01752 304774

🖹 01752 304775

e-mail: enquiry@plymouthmuseum.gov.uk

Web: www.plymouthmuseum.gov.uk

Dir: *off A38 onto A374, museum on NW of city centre, opposite university*

The City Museum & Art Gallery is home to a Fine and Decorative Art Collection of paintings, prints and Reynolds family portraits, silver and Plymouth China, and the Cottonian Collection of drawings, sculpture and books. There is a lively programme of art exhibitions, as well as archaeology and history displays, and a 'hands-on' children's section.

Times: Open all year, Tue-Fri 10-5.30, Sat & BH Mon 10-5. Closed Good Fri & 25-26 Dec.

Facilities: Ⓟ (200yds) (time restricted on-street parking) ⊓ & (wheelchair available), toilets for disabled, shop ⊗ (ex assist dogs)

YELVERTON

Yelverton Paperweight Centre

4 Buckland Terrace, Leg O'Mutton Corner, PL20 6AD

☎ 01822 854250

🖹 01822 854250

e-mail: paperweightcentre@btinternet.com

Web: www.paperweightcentre.co.uk

Dir: *at Yelverton off A386, Plymouth to Tavistock road*

This unusual centre is the home of the Broughton Collection - a glittering permanent collection of glass paperweights of all sizes and designs. The centre also has an extensive range of modern glass paperweights for sale. Prices range from a few pounds to over £1000. There is also a series of oil and water-colour paintings by talented local artists.

Times: *Open Apr-Oct, daily 10.30-5; 10-24 Dec, daily; Nov & Jan-Mar by appointment.

Facilities: Ⓟ (100yds) & (ramp on request), shop, tours available ▭ (advance booking requested)

DEVON

DORSET

CHRISTCHURCH
**Christchurch Castle &
Norman House**

Web: www.english-heritage.org.uk

Dir: *near Christchurch Priory*

Set on the river bank, the ruins of this Norman keep and constable's house date back to the 12th century.

Times: Open at any reasonable time.

Facilities: 🚌 ♿

CHRISTCHURCH
Red House Museum & Gardens

Quay Road, BH23 1BU

☎ 01202 482860

🖷 01202 481924

Web: www.hants.gov.uk/museum/redhouse

Dir: *follow brown tourist signs from Christchurch, Red House is on corner of Quay Rd*

Local history, archaeology and natural history is displayed in a beautiful Georgian house. Excellent costume collection, some Arthur Romney-Green furniture and gardens with a woodland walk and herb garden. Regularly changing temporary exhibitions of contemporary art and crafts.

Times: *Open Tue-Sat 10-5, Sun 2-5 (last admission 4.30). Open BHs (spring & summer) Closed 25 Dec-1 Jan & Good Fri.

Facilities: Ⓟ (200yds) 🍽 ♿ (hearing aid and loop in reception only), toilets for disabled (ground floor access to toilets). shop ⊗ (ex assist dogs) 🚌 (must pre-book)

DORCHESTER
Maiden Castle
DT1 9PR

Web: www.english-heritage.org.uk
Dir: *2m S of Dorchester, access off A354, N of bypass*

The Iron Age fort ranks among the finest in Britain. It covers 47 acres, and has daunting earthworks, with a complicated defensive system around the entrances. One of its main purposes may well have been to protect grain from marauding bands. The first single-rampart fort dates from around 700BC, and by 100BC the earthworks covered the whole plateau. It was finally overrun by Roman troops in AD43.

Times: Open at any reasonable time.
Facilities: ℗ 🚌 ⌗

POOLE
Waterfront Museum
4 High St, BH15 1BW
☎ 01202 262600
🖺 01202 262622
e-mail: museums@poole.gov.uk
Web: www.boroughofpoole.com/museums
Dir: *off Poole Quay*

The Waterfront Museum tells the story of Poole's history, including the Studland Bay wreck and trade with Newfoundland with displays and hands-on activities. The museum re-opens after major refurbishment in summer 2007. Please contact the Poole Museums Service for further information.

Times: Please telephone for opening times
Facilities: ℗ (250yds) ♿ (Scaplen's Court not accessible), toilets for disabled, shop ⊗ (ex assist dogs) 🚌

DORSET

DORSET/CO DURHAM

TOLPUDDLE

Tolpuddle Martyrs Museum

DT2 7EH

☎ 01305 848237

🖷 01305 848237

e-mail: jpickering@tuc.org.uk

Web: www.tolpuddlemartyrs.org.uk

Dir: *off A35 from Dorchester, Tolpuddle is signed at Troytown turn off. Continue on old A35. Museum has brown heritage sign*

This interactive exhibition tells how the Tolpuddle Martyrs, six farm labourers, were transported to Australia for forming a trade union. The Tolpuddle Martyrs Festival is held on the weekend of the 3rd Sunday in July.

Times: Open all year, Apr-Oct, Tue-Sat 10-5, Sun 11-5; Nov-Mar, Thu-Sat 10-4, Sun 11-4, closed Mon-Wed. Closed 17 Dec-3 Jan. Open other BHs.

Facilities: ℗ (outside museum) ♿ (parking, interactive computers at wheelchair height), toilets for disabled, shop, audio commentaries available ⊗ (ex assist dogs) 🚌 (prior booking required)

BARNARD CASTLE

Egglestone Abbey

DL12 8QN

Web: www.english-heritage.org.uk

Dir: *1m S of Barnard Castle on minor road off B6277*

The scant, but charming remains of a small medieval monastery. The picturesque ruins of Egglestone are located above a bend in the River Tees. A large part of the church can be seen, as can remnants of monastic buildings.

Times: Open daily, 10-6.

Facilities: ℗ ♿ 🚌 ⌗

BOWES
Bowes Castle
DL12 9LD
Web: www.english-heritage.org.uk
Dir: *in Bowes village, just off A66*
Massive ruins of Henry II's tower keep, three storeys high, set within the earthworks of a Roman fort and overlooking the valley of the River Greta.
Times: Open at any reasonable time.
Facilities: ⌂ & ⌗

DURHAM
Finchale Priory
Brasside, Newton Hall, DH1 5SH
☎ 0191 386 3828
Web: www.english-heritage.org.uk
Dir: *3m NE*
Dating from the 13th century, these beautiful priory ruins are in a wooded setting besides the River Wear.
Times: Please call keykeeper on 0191 386 6528
Facilities: ℗ (charged) ☕ shop 🚌 ⌗

CO DURHAM

SHILDON

Locomotion: The National Railway Museum at Shildon

DL4 1PQ

☎ 01388 777999

🖹 01388 777999

e-mail: gill@hamer-loco.fsnet.co.uk

Web: www.locomotion.uk.com

Dir: *A1(M) junct 68, take A68 & A6072 to Shildon, museum is 0.25m SE of town centre*

Timothy Hackwood (1786-1850) was an important figure in the development of steam travel. The museum and house detail his life and the steam transport revolution, displaying working models and locomotives from various periods. Steam train rides are available thoughout the year on event days. The Collections building contains 60 vehicles from the National Collection.

Times: *Telephone for details

Facilities: 🅿 🅟 (500yds) ⛲ 🍴 ♿ (bus available to transport guests, please contact), toilets for disabled, shop, tours available ⊗ (ex assist dogs) 🚌

HADLEIGH

Hadleigh Castle

☎ 01760 755161

Web: www.english-heritage.org.uk

Dir: *0.75m S of A13*

The subject of several of Constable's paintings, the castle has fine views of the Thames estuary. It is defended by ditches on three sides, and the north-east and south-east towers are still impressive.

Times: Open at any reasonable time.

Facilities: (limited access due to hilly surroundings) 🚌 ⚏

MISTLEY
Mistley Towers
CO11 1NJ
☎ 01206 393884
Web: www.english-heritage.org.uk
Dir: *on B1352, 1.5m E of A137 at Lawford*
All that remains of the grand hall and church, designed by Robert Adam, are the lodges built in 1782 for the hall, and two square towers, topped with drums and domes which came from an earlier church.
Times: Open all reasonable times. Key available from Mistley Quay Workshops 01206 393884
Facilities: ♿ 🚍

WALTHAM ABBEY
Waltham Abbey Gatehouse, Bridge & Entrance to Cloisters
☎ 01992 702200
Web: www.english-heritage.org.uk
Dir: *in Waltham Abbey off A112*
Beside the great Norman church at Waltham are the slight remains of the abbey buildings - bridge, gatehouse and part of the north cloister. The bridge is named after King Harold, founder of the abbey.
Times: Open at any reasonable time.
Facilities: ♿ (sensory trail guide) 🚍

ESSEX

DEERHURST
Odda's Chapel

Dir: *off B4213 near River Severn at Abbots Court SW of parish church*

This rare Saxon chapel was built by Earl Odda and dedicated in 1056. When it was discovered, it had been incorporated into a farmhouse. It has now been carefully restored.

Times: *Open Apr-Oct, daily 10-6; Nov-Mar, daily 10-4. Closed 24-26 Dec & 1 Jan.

Facilities: ❷ (Charged) ⊗ 🚌

GLOUCESTER
Gloucester Folk Museum

99-103 Westgate Street, GL1 2PG

☎ 01452 396868 & 396869

🖹 01452 330495

e-mail: folk.museum@gloucester.gov.uk

Web: www.gloucester.gov.uk

Dir: *from W - A40 & A48; from N - A38 & M5, from E - A40 & B4073; from S - A4173 & A38*

Three floors of splendid Tudor and Jacobean timber-framed buildings dating from the 16th and 17th centuries along with new buildings housing the Dairy, Ironmonger's shop and Wheelwright and Carpenter workshops. Local history, domestic life, crafts, trades and industries from 1500 to the present. Exhibitions, hands-on activities, events, demonstrations and role play sessions throughout the year.

Times: Open all year, Tue-Sat, 10-5

Facilities: ℗ (500yds) 🍴 ♿ (virtual tour in Protal gallery, induction loops), shop ⊗ (ex assist dogs) 🚌 (book in advance)

GLOUCESTER

Gloucester City Museum & Art Gallery

Brunswick Road, GL1 1HP

☎ 01452 396131

🖷 01452 410898

e-mail: city.museum@gloucester.gov.uk

Web: www.gloucester.gov.uk

Dir: *city centre*

An impressive range of Roman artefacts including the Rufus Sita tombstone; the amazing Iron Age Birdlip Mirror; one of the earliest backgammon sets in the world; dinosaur fossils; and paintings by artists such as Turner and Gainsborough. There is something for everyone. Exciting temporary exhibitions from contemporary art and textiles to dinosaurs and local history; children's activities and regular special events.

Times: Open all year, Tue-Sat 10-5.

Facilities: ℗ (500yds) ♿ (lift to 1st floor galleries, induction loops), toilets for disabled, shop ⊗ (ex assist dogs) 🚌 (advance booking)

ULEY

Uley Long Barrow (Hetty Pegler's Tump)

Web: www.english-heritage.org.uk

Dir: *3.5m NE of Dursley on B4066*

This 180ft Neolithic long barrow is popularly known as Hetty Pegler's Tump. The mound, surrounded by a wall, is about 85ft wide. It contains a stone central passage, and three burial chambers.

Times: Open at any reasonable time.

Facilities: 🚌 ⌗

GLOUCESTERSHIRE

GREATER MANCHESTER

ASHTON-UNDER-LYNE
Museum of The Manchester Regiment

The Town Hall, Market Place, OL6 6DL

☎ 0161 342 2812 & 3710

🖷 0161 343 2869

e-mail: portland.basin@tameside.gov.uk

Web: www.tameside.gov.uk

Dir: *in town centre, on market square, follow signs for museum*

The social and regimental history of the Manchester's is explored at this museum, tracing the story back to its origins in the 18th century. Children can try on military head-wear, experience a First World War trench, and try out the interactive 'A Soldier's Life'.

Times: *Open all year, Mon-Sat, 10-4. (Closed Sun).

Facilities: ℗ (50yds) (pay & display) ☕ lift, toilets for disabled ⊗ (ex assist dogs) 🚌 (must pre-book, max 50 people)

ASHTON-UNDER-LYNE
Portland Basin Museum

Portland Place, OL7 0QA

☎ 0161 343 2878

🖷 0161 343 2869

e-mail: portland.basin@tameside.gov.uk

Web: www.tameside.gov.uk

Dir: *M60 junct 23 into Ashton town centre. Museum is near Cross Hill Street & car park*

Exploring the social and industrial history of Tameside, this museum is part of the recently rebuilt Ashton Canal Warehouse, built in 1834. Visitors can walk around a 1920s street, dress up in old hats and gloves, steer a virtual canal boat, and see the original canal powered water-wheel that drove the warehouse machinery. Changing exhibitions and event programme.

Times: *Open all year, Tue-Sun 10-5. (Closed Mon, ex BHs).

Facilities: ℗ ℗ (100yds) 🍴 ⊼ ☕ grounds only access (wheelchair, lift, loop system), toilets for disabled on 2 floors, shop ⊗ (ex assist dogs) 🚌

ASHTON-UNDER-LYNE
Central Art Gallery

Central Library Building, Old Street, OL6 7SG

☎ 0161 342 2650

📄 0161 342 2650

e-mail: central.artgallery@tameside.gov.uk

Web: www.tameside.gov.uk

Dir: *Near centre of town, off A635*

Set in a fine Victorian Gothic building, the Central Art Gallery has three areas, each of which offers a varied programme of temporary exhibitions. A range of tastes and styles are covered, with group and solo shows of work by artists from the region including paintings, sculpture, installation and textiles. Holiday activities available for families.

Times: *Open all year, Tue, Wed & Fri 10-12.30 & 1-5; Thu 1-7.30 & Sat 9-12.30 & 1-4.

Facilities: Ⓟ (100yds) (pay and display) ♿ (induction loop), toilets for disabled, shop ⊗ (ex assist dogs) 🚌

MANCHESTER
The Museum of Science and Industry in Manchester

Liverpool Road, Castlefield, M3 4FP

☎ 0161 832 2244 & 832 1830

📄 0161 833 1471

e-mail: marketing@msim.org.uk

Web: www.msim.org.uk

Dir: *follow brown tourist signs from city centre*

This museum is on the site of the world's oldest passenger railway station. Galleries packed full of fascinating facts and amazing artefacts bring the past to life. See the mind bending science centre, wheels of industry turning in the Power Hall, and the planes that made flying history. Changing exhibitions.

Times: *Open all year, daily 10-5. Last admission 4.30. Closed 24-26 Dec & 1 Jan. (Extended hrs for some special events)

Facilities: Ⓟ (charged) Ⓟ (10 mins walk) 🖥 ⦿ (licensed) 🚍 ♿ (lifts, wheelchair loan service), toilets for disabled, shop, tours available ⊗ (ex assist dogs) 🚌 (no coach parking)

GREATER MANCHESTER

MANCHESTER
John Rylands Library

150 Deansgate, M3 3EH

☎ 0161 834 5343

🖷 0161 834 5574

e-mail: jrul.special-collechais@manchester.ac.uk

Web: rylibweb.man.ac.uk/spcoll/

Dir: *on Deansgate, in city centre, A56. Situated next to the Manchester Evening News Building*

Founded as a memorial to Manchester cotton-magnate and millionaire John Rylands, this is a public library, and also the Special Collections Division of the John Rylands University Library of Manchester. World renowned, it extends to two million books, manuscripts and archival items.

Times: Telephone for opening times

Facilities: Ⓟ (400yds) (pay and display) ⬚ ground floor only access, shop, tours available, audio commentaries available ⊗ (ex assist dogs by arrangement) 🚌 (prior notice required)

MANCHESTER
Manchester Museum

The University, Oxford Road, M13 9PL

☎ 0161 275 2634 & 2643

🖷 0161 275 2676

e-mail: anna.j.davey@man.ac.uk

Web: www.museum.man.ac.uk

Dir: *S of city centre on B5117*

The Manchester Museum has leading research facilities and collections in archaeology, botany, Egyptology, ethnology, mineralogy, numismatics, and zoology, among others. There are large galleries devoted to most of these departments, but the Egyptology collection is particularly impressive, and includes mummies excavated by Sir William Flinders Petrie.

Times: *Open all year, Mon-Sat 10-5, Sun & BHs 11-4.

Facilities: Ⓟ (charged) Ⓟ ⬚ ㅠ ♿ (lift access, hearing loop, accessible parking), toilets for disabled, shop ⊗ (ex assist dogs) 🚌 (pre-booking required)

MANCHESTER
The Whitworth Art Gallery

The University of Manchester, Oxford Road, M15 6ER

☎ 0161 275 7450

▤ 0161 275 7451

e-mail: whitworth@manchester.ac.uk

Web: www.manchester.ac.uk/whitworth

Dir: *follow brown tourist signs, on Oxford Rd (B5117) to S of city centre. Gallery in Whitworth Park, opp Manchester Royal Infirmary*

The gallery houses an impressive range of modern and historic drawings, prints, paintings and sculpture, as well as the largest collection of textiles and wallpapers outside London, and an internationally famous collection of British watercolours. Touring exhibitions and lectures.

Times: *Open Mon-Sat 10-5, Sun 2-5. Closed Good Fri & Xmas-New Year.

Facilities: ❷ ⓟ (on road) (car park full at peak times) ♊ ☴ ♿ (wheelchair available, induction loop, Braille lift buttons), toilets for disabled, shop ⊗ (ex assist dogs) ▄▄ (with prior notice)

MANCHESTER
Gallery of Costume

Platt Hall, Rusholme, M14 5LL

☎ 0161 224 5217

▤ 0161 256 3278

e-mail: a.jarvis@notes.manchester.gov.uk

Dir: *situated in Platt Fields Park, Rusholme, access from Wilmslow Rd. 2m S of city centre*

With one of the most comprehensive costume collections in Great Britain, this gallery makes captivating viewing. Housed in a fine Georgian mansion, the displays focus on the changing styles of everyday fashion and accessories over the last 400 years. Contemporary fashion is also illustrated. Due to the vast amount of material in the collection, no one period is permanently displayed.

Times: *Open to public on last Sat of month. Mon-Fri by appointment, please ring 0161 224 5217

Facilities: ❷ ♿ shop ⊗ (ex assist dogs) ▄▄

GREATER MANCHESTER

GREATER MANCHESTER

MANCHESTER
Manchester Art Gallery
Mosley St, M2 3JL
☎ 0161 235 8888
📄 0161 235 8899
Web: www.manchestergalleries.org
Dir: *from M60 follow signs to city centre, gallery close to Town Hall and Central Library*
Housing the city's magnificent art collection in stunning Victorian and contemporary surroundings, highlights include Pre-Raphaelite works, crafts and design, and early 20th-century British art. The Clore Interactive Gallery has lively exhibits and multimedia facilities. There is also a wide range of events.
Times: Open Tue-Sun, 10-5 (closed Mon except BH). Closed Good Fri, 24-26 & 31 Dec & 1 Jan.
Facilities: ℗ (NCP-5 mins walk) ⌨ 🍴 (licensed) ♿ wheelchairs, induction loops, audio guides, toilets for disabled, shop, tours available, audio commentaries available ⊗ (ex assist dogs) 🚌 (pre-booking essential)

MANCHESTER
Imperial War Museum North
The Quays, Trafford Wharf Road, Trafford Park, M17 1TZ
☎ 0161 836 4000
📄 0161 836 4012
e-mail: info@iwmnorth.org.uk
Web: www.iwm.org.uk
Dir: *M60 junct 9, join Parkway (A5081) towards Trafford Park. At 1st island take 3rd exit onto Village Way. At next island take 2nd exit. Right at T-junct onto Trafford Wharf Rd. Or, leave M602 junct 2 and follow signs*
This war museum is built to resemble three shards of a shattered globe, representing conflict on land, sea, and in the air.
Times: Open daily Mar-Oct 10-6, Nov-Feb 10-5. Closed 24-26 Dec.
Facilities: ⊖ (charged) ℗ (15 min walk) ( ) ⌨ (licensed) 🚻 ♿ (lifts, parking, wheelchairs, Braille sign in lift), toilets for disabled on ground floor, shop, tours available ⊗ (ex assist dogs) 🚌 (pre-booked only)

MANCHESTER
Urbis

Cathedral Gardens, M4 3BG

☎ 0161 605 8200

🖹 0161 605 8201

e-mail: info@urbis.org.uk

Web: www.urbis.org.uk

Dir: *opposite to Victoria Railway Station*

Urbis explores the dynamic culture of the modern city. The top three floors of interactive exhibits explore cities around the world from Tokyo to Paris, revealing how different cities work, how they change and how they affect others.

Times: *Open daily, Sun-Wed, 10-6; Thu-Sat, 10-8.

Facilities: ⓟ (200yds) ⌻ (licensed) ♿ toilets for disabled, shop, tours available ⊗ (ex assist dogs) 🚌 (advance booking required)

PRESTWICH
Heaton Park

Heaton Park, M25 2SW

☎ 0161 773 1085

🖹 0161 798 0107

e-mail: heatonpark@manchester.gov.uk

Web: www.manchester.gov.uk/leisure/parks

Dir: *4m N of Manchester city centre. M60 junct 19, S on A576, onto A6044 and A665, into St Margaret's Road. Park 100yds on R*

600 acres of rolling parkland on the edge of Manchester; a traditional park for the whole family. Facilities include a Tram Museum, sports pitches, stables, farm and animals centres, and a horticultural centre. The house has magnificent period interiors decorated with fine plasterwork, paintings and furniture.

Times: Park: Open all year daily; Hall: Open early Apr-early Oct, Wed-Sun & BH 11-5.30

Facilities: ⓟ (charged) ⓟ (100yds) (parking charged wknds only) ⌻ 🄰 ♿ toilets for disabled (100yds from house), shop, tours available ⊗ (ex assist dogs) 🚌

GREATER MANCHESTER

SALFORD
Salford Museum & Art Gallery
Peel Park, Crescent, M5 4WU
☎ 0161 736 2649
🖷 0161 745 9490
e-mail: salford.museum@salford.gov.uk
Web: www.salfordmuseum.org
Dir: *from N, M60 junct 13, A666. From S follow signs from end of M602. On A6*
The museum features a reconstruction of a 19th-20th century northern street with original shop fronts. Upstairs in the galleries there are temporary exhibitions, paintings, sculptures and ceramics. Spectacular Pilkington's display and hands-on activities.
Times: *Open all year Mon-Fri 10-4.45, Sat & Sun 1-5. Closed Good Fri, Etr Sat, 25 & 26 Dec, 1 Jan.
Facilities: ❷ ℗ (0.25m) ⌑ ⬥ (Braille & large print labels & visitor packs, hearing loop), toilets for disabled, shop, tours available, audio commentaries available ⊗ (ex assist dogs) 🚌 (must pre-book)

SALFORD
The Lowry
Pier Eight, Salford Quays, M50 3AZ
☎ 0870 787 5774
🖷 0161 876 2001
e-mail: info@thelowry.com
Web: www.thelowry.com
Dir: *M60 junct 12 for M602. Salford Quays is 0.25m from junct 3 of M602, follow brown Lowry signs*
The Lowry is an award-winning building housing galleries, shops, cafés and a restaurant, plus two theatres showing everything from West End plays and musicals, comedians, ballet and live bands. With regular family activity too, you can make a whole day of your visit.
Times: *Open daily from 10. Galleries, Sun-Fri from 11, Sat from 10. Closed 25 Dec.
Facilities: ❷ (charged) ℗ (150 yds) ⌑ ⑩ (licensed) ⬥ (Sennheiser System), toilets for disabled, shop ⊗ (ex assist dogs) 🚌 (pre-booking advised)

GREATER MANCHESTER

STALYBRIDGE

Astley Cheetham Art Gallery

Trinity Street, GK15 2BN

☎ 0161 338 6767

e-mail: astley.cheetham@tameside.gov.uk

Web: www.tameside.gov.uk

Dir: *N of town centre*

Built as a gift to the town in 1901 by mill owner John Frederick Cheetham, this one-time lecture hall has been an art gallery since 1932 when Cheetham left his collection to the town. Among the works are Italian paintings from the Renaissance, British masters such as Cox and Burne-Jones, and more recent gifts such as works by Turner and local artist Harry Rutherford. The gallery hosts a programme of temporary exhibitions of the collection and regional artists, and a variety of workshops are run for families throughout the year.

Times: *Open all year, Mon-Wed & Fri 10-12.30, 1-5; Sat 9-12.30, 1-4.

Facilities: Ⓟ (2hrs on street parking) ♿ (induction loop) Ⓧ (ex assist dogs) 🚌

STOCKPORT

Hat Works Museum

Wellington Mill, Wellington Road South, SK3 0EU

☎ 0845 833 0975

🖨 0161 480 8735

e-mail: bookings.hatworks@stockport.gov.uk

Web: www.hatworks.org.uk

Dir: *M60 junct 1, follow signs for town centre. Museum opposite bus station*

The UK's only museum of the hatting industry. See how hats are made with a unique working collection of Victorian millinery machinery and take a tour with expert guides who will give visitors an insight into the Hatter's World. Browse an extensive collection of hats before relaxing in the Level 2 café. Exhibitions and events throughout the year, contact for details.

Times: *Open daily Mon-Fri 10-5, Sat, Sun & BHs 1-5. (Telephone for Xmas opening times)

Facilities: Ⓟ (5min walk) (limited pay & display parking) 🎧♿ (hearing loops), toilets for disabled, shop, tours available Ⓧ (ex assist dogs) 🚌 (pre-booking essential)

HAMPSHIRE

FAREHAM
Royal Armouries Fort Nelson
Portsdown Hill Road, PO17 6AN

☎ 01329 233734

🖹 01329 822092

e-mail: fnenquiries@armouries.org.uk

Web: www.royalarmouries.org

Dir: *from M27 junct 11, follow brown tourist signs for Royal Armouries*

Home to the Royal Armouries' collection of over 350 big guns and cannon, this superbly restored fort overlooks Portsmouth Harbour. Built in the 1860s, it has secret tunnels, underground chambers and grass ramparts.

Times: Open Apr-Oct, daily 10-5 (Tue 11-5); Nov-Mar, daily 10.30-4 (Tue 11.30-4)

Facilities: ❷ (disabled parking on same side as fort) 🖵 (licensed) 🚪 ♿ (access & audio guide, ramps, induction loop, wheelchair), toilets for disabled (radar key), shop, tours available, audio commentaries available ⊗ (ex assist dogs) 🚌 (pre-booking advised for catering)

NETLEY
Netley Abbey
SO31 5FB

☎ 02392 581059

Web: www.english-heritage.org.uk

Dir: *4m SE of Southampton, facing Southampton Water*

A romantic ruin, set among green lawns and trees, this 13th-century Cistercian abbey was founded by Peter des Roches, tutor to Henry III. Nearby is the 19th century Gothic Netley Castle.

Times: Open all year, Apr-Sep, daily 10-6; Oct-Mar, daily 10-4

Facilities: ❷ ♿ ⊗ 🚌 ⛬

PORTSMOUTH
Eastney Beam Engine House

Henderson Rd, Eastney, PO4 9JF

☎ 023 9282 7261

🖹 023 9287 5276

e-mail: mvs@portsmouthcc.gov.uk

Web: www.portsmouthmuseums.co.uk

Dir: *accessible from A3(M), A27 & A2030, turn left at Bransbury Park traffic lights*

The main attraction here is a magnificent pair of James Watt Beam Engines still housed in their original High-Victorian engine house opened in 1887. One of these engines is in steam when the museum is open. A variety of other pumping engines, many in running order are also on display.

Times: *Open last wknd of month, 1-5 (last admission 30 minutes before closing). (Closed Aug & Dec).

Facilities: ℗ (300yds) shop ⊗ (ex assist dogs) 🚌 (telephone in advance)

PORTSMOUTH
City Museum & Records Office

Museum Rd, PO1 2LJ

☎ 023 9282 7261

🖹 023 9287 5276

e-mail: mvs@portsmouthcc.gov.uk

Web: www.portsmouthcitymuseums.co.uk/

Dir: *M27/M275 into Portsmouth, follow museum symbol signs*

Dedicated to local history, fine and decorative art, 'The Story of Portsmouth' displays room settings showing life here from the 17th century to the 1950s. The 'Portsmouth at Play' exhibition features leisure pursuits from the Victorian period to the 1970s. There is an art gallery, plus a temporary exhibition gallery. Official city records from the 14th century.

Times: *Open all year, Apr-Oct daily 10-5.30; Nov-Mar daily 10-5. Closed 24-26 Dec and Record Office closed on public holidays.

Facilities: ℗ ℗ (200yds) 🔲 🛋 ♿ (induction loops, lift & wheelchairs, parking), toilets for disabled, shop ⊗ (ex assist dogs) 🚌 (pre-booking)

HAMPSHIRE

HAMPSHIRE

PORTSMOUTH
Natural History Museum & Butterfly House

Cumberland House, Eastern Parade, PO4 9RF

☎ 023 9282 7261

▤ 023 9282 5276

e-mail: mvc@portsmouthcc.gov.uk

Web: www.portsmouthnaturalhistory.co.uk

Dir: *accessed via A3(M), A27 or A2030, follow signs to seafront*

Focusing on the natural history and geology of the area, with wildlife dioramas including a riverbank scene with fresh water aquarium. During the summer British and European butterflies fly free in the Butterfly House.

Times: *Open all year daily, Apr-Oct 10-5.30; Nov-Mar 10-5.

Facilities: Ⓟ (200yds) shop ⊗ (ex assist dogs) 🚌 (pre-booking)

SOUTHAMPTON
Museum of Archaeology

God's House Tower, Winkle Street, SO14 2NY

☎ 023 8063 5904 & 8083 2768

▤ 023 8033 9601

e-mail: museums@southampton.gov.uk

Web: www.southampton.gov.uk/leisure

Dir: *near the waterfront close to Queen's Park and the Town Quay*

The museum housed in an early fortified building, dating from the 1400s and taking its name from the nearby medieval hospital. Exhibits on the Roman, Saxon and medieval towns of Southampton are displayed.

Times: Open Tue-Fri 10-4, Sat 10-12, 1-4, Sun 1-4

Facilities: Ⓟ (400 yds) (designated areas only, parking charges) ground floor only access, shop, tours available ⊗ (ex assist dogs) 🚌 (pre-booking)

SOUTHAMPTON
Southampton Maritime Museum

The Wool House, Town Quay, SO14 2AR

☎ 023 8022 3941 & 8063 5904

▤ 023 8033 9601

e-mail: museums@southampton.gov.uk

Web: www.southampton.gov.uk/leisure

Dir: *on the waterfront, near to the Town Quay*

The Wool House was built in the 14th century as a warehouse for wool, and now houses a maritime museum, with models and displays telling the history of the Victorian and modern port of Southampton. There are exhibitions of the Titanic, The Queen Mary and an interactive area for children.

Times: Open Tue-Fri 10-4; Sat 10-1 & 2-4; Sun 1-4

Facilities: ℗ (400yds) (metered parking adjacent) ♿ (hearing loop on Titanic presentation), shop, audio commentaries available ⊗ (ex assist dogs) 🚌 (pre-booking)

SOUTHAMPTON
Southampton City Art Gallery

Civic Centre, Commercial Rd, SO14 7LP

☎ 023 8083 2277

▤ 023 8083 2153

e-mail: art.gallery@southampton.gov.uk

Web: www.southampton.gov.uk/art

Dir: *situated on the Watts Park side of the Civic Centre, a short walk from the station.*

The largest gallery in the south of England, with the finest collection of contemporary art in the country outside London. Varied displays of landscapes, portrait paintings or recent British art are always available, as well as a special display selected by members of the public.

Times: Open all year, Tue-Sat 10-5, Sun 1-4. Closed 25-27 & 31 Dec.

Facilities: ℗ (50yds) (nearby street parking is 1hr only) ⬚🍽♿ (free BSL signed tours by arrangement, 'touch tour') toilets for disabled, shop, tours available ⊗ (ex assist dogs) 🚌 (over 50 people, call ahead of visit)

HAMPSHIRE

HAMPSHIRE

TITCHFIELD
Titchfield Abbey

Place House Studio, Mill Lane, Fareham, PO15 5RA

☎ 01329 842133

Dir: *0.5m N off Titchfield, off A27*

Also known as 'Place House', in Tudor times this was the seat of the Earl of Southampton, built on the site of the abbey founded in 1232. He incorporated the gatehouse and the nave of the church into his house.

Times: *Open Apr-Sep, daily 10-6; Oct, daily 10-5; Nov-Mar, daily 10-4. Closed 25 Dec.

Facilities: ℗ ⌂ ♿ 🚌 (no coaches on site)

WINCHESTER
Royal Hampshire Regiment Museum & Memorial

Serle's House, Southgate Street, SO23 9EG

☎ 01962 863658

e-mail: serleshouse@aol.com

Web: www.royalhampshireregimentmuseum-um.co.uk

Dir: *Museum near city centre, 150yds from traffic lights in High St*

Regimental Museum of the Royal Hampshire Regiment 1702-1992, set in an 18th-century house by the regiment's Memorial Garden. The museum tells the history of the regiment, its regulars, militia, volunteers and Territorials.

Times: *Normally open all year (ex 2 wks Xmas & New Year), Mon-Fri 10-4; Apr-Oct wknds & BH 12-4.

Facilities: ℗ (1000yds) ♿ shop, tours available ⊗ (ex assist dogs) 🚌 (by appointment only)

WINCHESTER
The Great Hall

Castle Avenue, SO23 8PJ

☎ 01962 846476

▤ 01962 841326

e-mail: the.great.hall@hants.gov.uk

Web: www.hants.gov.uk/discover/places/great-hall.html

Dir: *top of High St.*

The only surviving part of Winchester Castle, once home to the Domesday Book, this 13th-century hall was the centre of court and government life. Built between 1222-1235 during the reign of Henry III, it is one of the finest five bay halls surviving in England. The Round Table based on the Arthurian Legend (built between 1230-1280) hangs in the hall. Queen Eleanor's Garden is a recreation of a medieval herborium.

Times: Open all year, Mar-Oct daily 10-5; Nov-Feb, daily 10-5, wknds 10-4. Closed 25-26 Dec.

Facilities: ℗ (200yds) ♿ toilets for disabled, shop, tours available ⊗ (ex assist dogs) ▰ (no coach parking)

WINCHESTER
Horsepower, The King's Royal Hussars

Peninsula Barracks, Romsey Road, SO23 8TS

☎ 01962 828539 & 828541

▤ 01962 828538

e-mail: beresford@krhmuseum.freeserve.co.uk

Web: www.krh.org.uk

Dir: *M3 junct 9/10 follow signs for city centre, then hospital A&E red signs to Romsey Road. Vehicle access is from Romsey Road.*

The museum tells the story of the Royal Hussars, formed by the amalgamation of two regiments raised at the time of the Jacobite Rebellion in 1715, the 10th Royal Hussars and the 11th Hussars. Now reopened after a major refurbishment.

Times: Open Tue-Fri 10-12.45, 1.15-4. Sat, Sun & BHs 12-4.

Facilities: ℗ ℗ (400yds) (limited spaces on wkdays) ⊡ ♿ (lift to first floor), toilets for disabled, shop ⊗ (ex assist dogs) ▰ (appointment only)

HAMPSHIRE

HEREFORDSHIRE

HEREFORD
Old House

High Town, HR1 2AA

☎ 01432 260694

📄 01432 342492

e-mail: herefordmuseums@herefordshire.gov.uk

Web: www.herefordshire.gov.uk

Dir: *located in the centre of the High Town*

The Old House is a fine Jacobean building dating from around 1621, and was once in a row of similar houses. The rooms are furnished in 17th-century style and give visitors the chance to learn what life was like in Cromwell's time.

Times: *Open all year, 10-5. Apr-Sep, Tue-Sat 10-5, Sun & BH Mon 10-4.

Facilities: ℗ (400yds) ♿ (virtual tour, Braille guide, tactile images,), shop, tours available, audio commentaries available ⊗ (ex assist dogs) 🚌 (prior notice)

BERKHAMSTED
Berkhamsted Castle

HP4 1HF

Web: www.english-heritage.org.uk

Dir: *by Berkhamsted station*

Roads and a railway have cut into the castle site, but its huge banks and ditches remain impressive. The original motte-and-bailey was built after the Norman Conquest, and there is a later stone keep, owned by the Black Prince, eldest son of King Edward III, where King John of France was imprisoned.

Times: Open all year, Summer, daily 10-6; Winter, daily 10-4. Closed 25 Dec & 1 Jan.

Facilities: 🚌 ⚏

LETCHWORTH
Museum & Art Gallery

Broadway, Garden City, SG6 3PF

☎ 01462 685647

🖷 01462 481879

e-mail: letchworth.museum@north-herts.gov.uk

Web: www.north-herts.gov.uk

Dir: *situated next door to Public Library, in town centre, near Broadway Cinema*

Opened in 1914 to house the collections of the Letchworth Naturalists' Society, this friendly town-centre museum has exhibits on local wildlife, geology, arts and crafts, and archaeology. There is also a museum shop and a regular programme of art exhibitions and workshops.

Times: *Open all year Mon-Tue, Thu-Sat (Closed BHs), 10-5.

Facilities: ℗ (100yds) ♿ (ramp, touch screen computer), shop, tours available ⊗ (ex assist dogs) 🚌 (coach parking is limited)

ST ALBANS
Museum of St Albans

9A Hatfield Road, AL1 3RR

☎ 01727 819340

🖷 01727 837472

e-mail: history@stalbans.gov.uk

Web: www.stalbansmuseums.org.uk

Dir: *city centre on A1057, Hatfield Road*

Exhibits include the Salaman collection of craft tools, and reconstructed workshops. The history of St Albans is traced from the departure of the Romans up to the present day. There is a special exhibition gallery with a surprising variety of exhibitions and a wildlife garden with picnic area.

Times: *Open all year, daily 10-5, Sun 2-5. Closed 25-26 Dec.

Facilities: ℗ ℗ (0.5m) 🪑 ♿ toilets for disabled, shop ⊗ (ex assist dogs) 🚌 (no coach parking on site, pre-book)

HEREFORDSHIRE

HEREFORDSHIRE/ISLE OF WIGHT

TRING

The Walter Rothschild Zoological Museum

Akeman Street, HP23 6AP

☎ 020 7942 6171

🖹 020 7942 6150

e-mail: tring-enquiries@nhm.ac.uk

Web: www.nhm.ac.uk/museum/tring

Dir: *signed from A41*

An unusual museum, founded in the 1890s by Lionel Walter, 2nd Baron Rothschild, scientist, eccentric and natural history enthusiast. Now part of the Natural History Museum, it houses more than 4000 specimens from whales to fleas, and humming birds to tigers.

Times: Open all year, Mon-Sat 10-5, Sun 2-5. Closed 24-26 Dec.

Facilities: ❷ ℗ (on street) 🍽 🎭 ♿ (ramps, virtual tour, disabled parking space), toilets for disabled, shop ⊗ (ex assist dogs) 🚌 (no parking at site, must park in town)

BRIGHSTONE

Brighstone Shop and Museum

North Street, PO30 4AX

☎ 01983 740689

🖹 01983 740689

e-mail: isleofwight@nationaltrust.org.uk

Web: www.nationaltrust.org.uk/isleofwight

Dir: *off B3399 in Brighstone onto North Street, next to Post Office*

Situated within a row of attractive, thatched cottages you will find this museum which contains an evocative tableau and an interesting exhibition on village life in the 19th century.

Times: *Open 28 May-1 Oct daily. Mon-Sat 10-5. Sun 12-5. 2 Oct-23 Dec. Mon-Sat 10-4. 28-30 Dec Thu-Sat 10-1.

Facilities: ℗ (100m) ♿ (hearing loop), shop ⊗ (ex assist dogs) 🚌 🌿

CANTERBURY

Royal Museum & Art Gallery with Buffs Museum

High Street, CT1 2RA

☎ 01227 452747

🖷 01227 455047

e-mail: museums@canterbury.gov.uk

Web: www.canterbury-artgallery.co.uk

Dir: *in Beaney Institute (1st floor) in High St*

A splendid Victorian building, houses decorative arts and the city's picture collections- including a gallery for T.S. Cooper, England finest cattle painter. The art gallery is the major space in the area for the visual arts with a varied exhibition programme. Here too is the Buffs Museum, which tells the story of one of England's oldest infantry regiments and its worldwide service.

Times: *Open all year, Mon-Sat 10-5. Closed Good Fri, BH and Xmas period. (Last admission 4.45)

Facilities: Ⓟ (500yds), shop ⊗ (ex assist dogs) 🚌 (pre-booked preferred)

EYNSFORD

Eynsford Castle

Web: www.english-heritage.org.uk

Dir: *in Eynsford, off A225*

One of the first stone castles to be built by the Normans. The moat and remains of the curtain wall and hall can still be seen.

Times: Open Apr-mid Jul & early Aug-Sep, daily 10-6; Oct-Nov, daily, 10-4; Dec-Jan, Wed-Sun, 10-4; Feb-Mar, daily, 10-4. Closed 24-26 Dec and 1 Jan. NB. Mid Jul-early Aug property may be closed for live events, tickets to be booked.

Facilities: Ⓟ ♿ 🚌 ⚏

KENT

KENT

MAIDSTONE
Tyrwhitt Drake Museum of Carriages

The Archbishop's Stables, Mill Street, ME15 6YE

☎ 01622 602838

e-mail: museuminfo@maidstone.gov.uk

Web: www.museum.maidstone.gov.uk

Dir: *close to River Medway & Archbishops Palace, just off A229 in town centre*

The museum is home to a unique collection of horse-drawn vehicles and transport curiosities. More than 60 vehicles are on display, from grand carriages and ornate sleighs to antique sedan chairs and Victorian cabs, and there is even an original ice-cream cart.

Times: Open May-mid Sep, 10.30-4.30

Facilities: ℗ (50yds) ♿ shop, tours available ⊗ (ex assist dogs) 🚌

MAIDSTONE
Maidstone Museum & Bentlif Art Gallery

St Faith's Street, ME14 1LH

☎ 01622 602838

e-mail: museum@maidstone.gov.uk

Web: www.museum.maidstone.gov.uk

Dir: *close to County Hall & Maidstone East railway station, opposite Fremlin's Walk*

Set in an Elizabethan manor house which has been much extended over the years, this museum houses an outstanding collection of fine and applied arts, including watercolours, furniture, ceramics, and a collection of Japanese art and artefacts. The museum of the Queen's Own Royal West Kent Regiment is also housed here. Please contact for details of temporary exhibitions, workshops etc.

Times: Open all year, Mon-Sat 10-5.15, Sun & BH Mon 11-4. Closed 25-26 Dec & 1 Jan

Facilities: ℗ (150 yds) ⊑ ♿ (lifts), shop ⊗ (ex assist dogs) 🚌

RECULVER

Reculver Towers & Roman Fort

Herne Bay, CT6 6SU

☎ 01227 740676

Web: www.english-heritage.org.uk

Dir: *3m E of Herne Bay*

An imposing 12th-century landmark: twin towers and the walls of a Roman fort.

Times: Open any reasonable time, external viewing only.

Facilities: ❷ ♿ (long slope from car park to fort) 🚌 ♯

ROCHESTER

Guildhall Museum

High Street, ME1 1PY

☎ 01634 848717

📄 01634 832919

e-mail: guildhall.museum@medway.gov.uk

Web: www.medway.gov.uk

Dir: *follow signs from A2 to Rochester city centre, museum is at N end of High St*

Housed in two adjacent buildings, one dating from 1687 and the other from 1909. The collections are arranged chronologically from Prehistory to the Victorian and Edwardian periods. They cover local history and archaeology, fine and decorative art. Also a gallery devoted to the River Medway prison hulks and a room detailing the links between Charles Dickens and the Medway Towns. Regular programme of temporary exhibitions.

Times: *Open all year, daily 10-4.30. (Last admission 4). Closed Xmas & New Year.

Facilities: ℗ (250 yds) ♿ shop ⊗ (ex assist dogs) 🚌 (pre-booking essential)

KENT

KENT

ROYAL TUNBRIDGE WELLS

Tunbridge Wells Museum and Art Gallery

Civic Centre, Mount Pleasant, TN1 1JN

☎ 01892 554171 & 526121

🖨 01892 554131

e-mail: museum@tunbridgewells.gov.uk

Web: www.tunbridgewellsmuseum.org

Dir: *adjacent to Town Hall, off A264*

This combined museum and art gallery tells the story of the borough of Tunbridge Wells. There are collections of costume, art, dolls and toys along with natural and local history from dinosaur bones to the original Pantiles. There is also a large collection of Tunbridge ware, the intricate wooden souvenirs made for visitors to the Wells. The art gallery features a changing programme of contemporary and historic art, touring exhibitions, and local art and craft.

Times: Open all year, daily 9.30-5. Sun 10-4. Closed BHs & Etr Sat.

Facilities: ℗ (200 yds) ♿ (parking adjacent to building), shop ⊗ (ex assist dogs) 🚌 (pre-booking)

WEST MALLING

St Leonard's Tower

ME19 6PE

☎ 01732 870872

Web: www.english-heritage.org.uk

Dir: *on unclass road W of A228*

Early example of a Norman tower keep, built c.1080 by Gundulf, Bishop of Rochester. The tower stands almost to its original height and takes its name from a chapel dedicated to St Leonard that once stood nearby.

Times: Open any reasonable time for exterior viewing. Contact West Malling Parish Council for interior viewing - 01732 870872.

Facilities: ♿ 🚌 ♿

CHORLEY

Astley Hall Museum & Art Gallery

Astley Park, PR7 1NP

☎ 01257 515555

🖷 01257 515923

e-mail: astley.hall@chorley.gov.uk

Web: www.astleyhall.co.uk

Dir: *M61 junct 8, signed Botany Bay. Follow brown signs*

A charming Tudor/Stuart building set in beautiful parkland, this lovely Hall retains a comfortable 'lived-in' atmosphere. There are pictures and pottery to see, as well as fine furniture and rare plasterwork ceilings. Special events throughout the year.

Times: *Open Apr (or Etr)-Oct, Sat-Sun & BH Mon 12-5; By appointment only during the week

Facilities: ℗ ℗ (200 yds) ⊼ ♿ (video of upper floors, print/Braille guide, CD audio guide) shop, tours available, audio commentaries available ⊗ (ex assist dogs) 🚌 (pre booked)

PRESTON

Harris Museum & Art Gallery

Market Square, PR1 2PP

☎ 01772 258248

🖷 01772 886764

e-mail: harris.museum@preston.gov.uk

Web: www.harrismuseum.org.uk

Dir: *M6 junct 31, follow signs for city centre, park at bus station car park*

An impressive Grade I listed Greek Revival building containing extensive collections of fine and decorative art including a gallery of Clothes and Fashion. The Story of Preston covers the city's history. Exhibitions of contemporary art and social history, plus events and activities throughout the year.

Times: *Open all year, Mon & Wed-Sat 10-5, Tues 11-5, Sun 11-4.

Facilities: ℗ (5 mins walk) (blue badge disabled parking only) ⊡ ♿ (wheelchair available, chair lift to mezzanine galleries), toilets for disabled (located on ground floor, radar key, shop ⊗ (ex guide & assist dogs) 🚌 (contact prior to visit)

LANCASHIRE

LANCASHIRE

PRESTON
The National Football Museum

Sir Tom Finney Way, Deepdale, PR1 6RY

☎ 01772 908442

🖨 01772 908444

e-mail: enquiries@nationalfootballmuseum.com

Web: www.nationalfootballmuseum.com

Dir: *2m from M6 juncts 31, 31A or 32. Follow brown tourist signs*

Deepdale Stadium is home to Preston North End, first winners of the professional football league in 1888-9. Fascinating trip through football past and present includes the FIFA Museum Collection, a fine display of memorabilia and artefacts; interactive displays, and virtual trips to every League ground. Also an art gallery dedicated to the Beautiful Game.

Times: *Open all year Tue-Sat 10-5, Sun 11-5. Closed Mon ex BHs and school hols. Contact for opening times on match days.

Facilities: ❷ ℗ (50yds) ☕ ♿ (lifts, multi-sensory exhibitions), toilets for disabled, shop ⊗ (ex assist dogs) 🚌

ROSSENDALE
Rossendale Museum

Whitaker Park, Haslingden Road, Rawtenstall, BB4 6RE

☎ 01706 244682

🖨 01706 250037

e-mail: rossendalemuseum@btconnect.com

Dir: *off A681, 0.25m W of Rawtenstall centre*

Former mill owner's house, built in 1840 and set in the delightful Whitaker Park. Displays include fine and decorative arts, a Victorian drawing room, natural history, costume, local and social history and regular temporary exhibitions.

Times: *Open Apr-Oct, Tue-Thu, Sat-Sun & BHs, 1-4.30; Nov-Mar, 1-4.

Facilities: ❷ ℗ 250yds (limited parking) ♿ (large print, audio guides, induction loop, lift) toilets for disabled, shop, tours available ⊗ (ex assist dogs) 🚌 (by arrangement)

SILVERDALE
Waterslack Farm Shop, Café, & Garden Centre
Ford Lane, LA5 0UH
☎ 01524 701255
▤ 01524 703047
e-mail: info@waterslack.com
Web: www.waterslack.com
Dir: *M6 junct 35, then A6 towards Milnthorpe. Turn off A6 at Nineteen Acre Lane & follow signs for Leighton Moss Nature Reserve. Pass Reserve, turn right at T-junct & follow signs*

With a beautiful plant section, unique Vesage arts and crafts collection, freshly made foods and stunning surroundings, Waterslack offers everything for your perfect day out. Come and see the many animals or enjoy a walk through one of the nature reserves around Waterslack.
Times: *Open Mar-Oct, Mon-Sat 9-6 & Sun 10-5; Nov-Feb, Mon-Sat 9-5
Facilities: ❷ ⊡ (licensed) ♿ toilets for disabled, shop, garden centre 🚌 (book in advance)

DONINGTON LE HEATH
Donington le Heath Manor House
Manor Road, Coalville, LE67 2FW
☎ 01530 831259
▤ 01530 831259
e-mail: museum@leics.gov.uk
Web: www.leics.gov.uk/museums
Dir: *S of Coalville*

This is a rare example of a medieval manor house, tracing its history back to about 1280. It has now been restored as a period house, with fine oak furnishings. The surrounding grounds include period gardens, and the adjoining stone barn houses a restaurant.
Times: Open Mar-Nov 11-4 daily, Dec-Feb Sat-Sun 11-4
Facilities: ❷ ⊡ ▦ (licensed) ⊞ ♿ toilets for disabled, shop, tours available, audio commentaries available ⊗ (ex assist dogs) 🚌 (max 50)

LEICESTERSHIRE

LEICESTER
The Record Office for Leicestershire

Long Street, Wigston Magna, LE18 2AH

☎ 0116 257 1080

🖹 0116 257 1120

e-mail: recordoffice@leics.gov.uk

Web: www.leics.gov.uk/museums

Dir: *old A50, S of Leicester*

Housed in a converted 19th-century school in Wigston, the Record Office holds photographs, electoral registers and archive film, files of local newspapers, history tapes and sound recordings, all of which can be studied.

Times: Open all year, Mon, Tue & Thu 9.15-5, Wed 9.15-7.30, Fri 9.15-4.45, Sat 9.15-12.15. Closed Sun & BH wknds Sat-Tue.

Facilities: 𝐏 ℗ ♿ toilets for disabled ⊗ (ex assist dogs)

LEICESTER
Belgrave Hall & Gardens

Church Road, off Thurcaston Rd, Belgrave, LE4 5PE

☎ 0116 266 6590

🖹 0116 261 3063

Web: www.leicester.gov.uk/museums

Dir: *off Belgrave/Loughborough road, 1m from city centre*

A delightful three-storey Queen Anne house dating from 1709 with beautiful period and botanic gardens. Authentic room settings contrast Georgian elegance with Victorian cosiness and include the kitchen, drawing room, music room and nursery.

Times: *Open all year, Apr-Sep, Mon-Sat 10-5, Sun 1-5; Oct-Mar, Mon-Sat 10-4, Sun 1-4. Closed 24-26 Dec & 31 Dec-1 Jan.

Facilities: 𝐏 ℗ ⊟ ♿ (loan of wheelchair), toilets for disabled, shop ⊗ (ex assist dogs)
🚌

LINCOLN
Usher Gallery

Lindum Road, LN2 1NN

☎ 01522 527980

📄 01522 560165

e-mail: usher.gallery@lincolnshire.gov.uk

Web: www.lincolnshire.gov.uk/usher

Dir: *in city centre, signed*

The Gallery houses Lincoln jeweller James Ward Usher's magnificent collection of watches, porcelain and miniatures, as well as topographical works, watercolours by Peter de Wint, Tennyson memorabilia and coins. Popular and changing display of contemporary visual arts and crafts. Lively lecture programme and children's activity diary.

Times: *Open all year, Tue-Sat 10-5 (last entry 4.30), Sun 1-5 (last entry 4.30), from 1 Jun daily 10-5. Open BHs. Closed 24-26 Dec & 1 Jan.

Facilities: 𝗣 ℗ (150yds) ⊑ 🎪 ♿ (large print guides, induction loop, parking), toilets for disabled, shop ⊗ (ex assist dogs) 🚌

STAMFORD
Stamford Museum

Broad Street, PE9 1PJ

☎ 01780 766317

📄 01780 480363

e-mail: stamford_museum@lincolnshire.gov.uk

Web: www.lincolnshire.gov.uk/stamfordmuseum

Dir: *from A1 follow town centre signs from any Stamford exit*

Displays illustrate the history of this fine stone town and include Stamford Ware pottery, the visit of Daniel Lambert and the Town's more recent industrial past. The new Stamford Tapestry depicts the history of the town in wool.

Times: Open all year, Apr-Sep, Mon-Sat 10-5, Sun 1-4; Oct-Mar Mon-Sat 10-5. Closed 24-26 & 31 Dec & 1 Jan.

Facilities: ℗ (200yds) (on street parking is limited waiting) ♿ (audio loop at reception, Braille leaflets), shop ⊗ (ex assist dogs) 🚌 (prior notice preferred)

LINCOLNSHIRE

LONDON

LONDON E2
V & A Museum of Childhood

Cambridge Heath Road, E2 9PA

☎ 020 8980 2415

🖹 020 8983 5225

e-mail: moc@vam.ac.uk

Web: www.museumofchildhood.org.uk

Dir: *Underground - Bethnal Green*

Following a £4.7 million transformation, the V&A Museum of Childhood has a stunning new entrance, fully updated galleries and displays, a brand new gallery and expanded public spaces. Galleries include Creativity, Moving Toys, World in the East End, Design in Focus, and Children in Trouble. There is also a full programme of activities.

Times: Open all year, daily 10-5.50, closed 25-26 Dec, 1 Jan.

Facilities: ℗ (metered parking) ⌷ (licensed) ⊟ ♿ (disabled parking by arrangement), toilets for disabled, shop, tours available ⊗ 🚍 (prior booking)

LONDON E2
Geffrye Museum

136 Kingsland Road, Shoreditch, E2 8EA

☎ 020 7739 9893

🖹 020 7729 5647

e-mail: info@geffrye-museum.org.uk

Web: www.geffrye-museum.org.uk

Dir: *S end of Kingsland Rd A10 in Shoreditch between Cremer St & Pearson St*

The only museum in the UK to specialise in the domestic interiors and furniture of the urban middle classes. Displays span the 400 years from 1600 to the present day. Set in elegant 18th-century buildings, surrounded by delightful gardens.

Times: *Open all year, Tue-Sat 10-5, Sun & BH Mon 12-5. Closed Mon, Good Fri, 24-26 Dec & New Year.

Facilities: ℗ (150yds) (meter parking, very restricted) 🍽 (licensed) 📱 ♿ (ramps, lift, wheelchair available, induction loop) toilets for disabled, shop, tours available, audio commentaries available ⊗ (ex assist dogs) 🚍 (booked in advance)

LONDON EC1

Wesley's Chapel, House & Museum

49 City Road, EC1Y 1AU

☎ 020 7253 2262

▤ 020 7608 3825

e-mail: museum@wesleyschapel.org.uk

Web: www.wesleyschapel.org.uk

Dir: *Underground - Old Street - exit number 4*

Wesley's Chapel has been the Mother Church of World Methodism since its construction in 1778. The crypt houses a museum which traces the development of Methodism from the 18th century to the present day. Wesley's house was built by him in 1779.

Times: Open all year, Mon-Sat , 10-4, Sun 12-2. Closed Thu 12.45-1.30, Xmas-New Year, BHs. (Last entry 30mins before closing).

Facilities: ℗ (5min) (NCP at Finsbury Square) ☵ ᕦ (lift to the crypt of the chapel) toilets for disabled, shop, tours available ⊗ (ex assist dogs) ▦ (max 50 people per party)

LONDON EC2

Museum of London

150 London Wall, EC2Y 5HN

☎ 0870 444 3851

▤ 0870 444 3853

e-mail: info@museumoflondon.org.uk

Web: www.museumoflondon.org.uk

Dir: *Underground - St Paul's, Barbican. N of St Paul's Cathedral at the end of St Martins le Grand and S of the Barbican. S of Aldersgate St*

Dedicated to the story of London and its people, the Museum of London exists to inspire a passion for London in all visitors. Permanent collection plus varied programme of major exhibitions and topical displays.

Times: *Open all year, Mon-Sat 10-5.50, Sun 12-5.50. Last admission 5.30.

Facilities: ❷ ℗ (NCP opp museum) (disabled/single decker coaches only) ⊡ (licensed) ☵ ᕦ (w/chairs & power scooters, lifts & induction loops), toilets for disabled, shop, audio commentaries available ⊗ (ex assist dogs) ▦ (free parking for coaches if pre-booked)

LONDON

LONDON

LONDON EC2
The Guildhall
Gresham Street, EC2V 5AE
☎ 020 7606 3030
📄 020 7260 1119
e-mail: pro@corpoflondon.gov.uk
Web: www.cityoflondon.gov.uk
Dir: *Underground - Bank, St Paul's*
The Court of Common Council (presided over by the Lord Mayor) administers the City of London and meets in the Guildhall, which dates from 1411. The great hall, traditionally used for the Lord Mayor's Banquet and other civic functions, is decorated with the banners and shields of the livery companies. The Clock Museum has 700 exhibits.
Times: *Open all year, May-Sep, daily 10-5; Oct-Apr, Mon-Sat 10-5. Closed Xmas, New Year, Good Fri, Etr Mon & infrequently for Civic occasions. Please contact 020 7606 3030 ext 1463 before visit to be certain of access.
Facilities: ℗ (NCP parking nearby) ♿ (lift for east and west crypts) toilets for disabled, shop ⊗ 🚌

LONDON EC2
Bank of England Museum
Bartholomew Lane, EC2R 8AH
☎ 020 7601 5545
📄 020 7601 5808
e-mail: museum@bankofengland.co.uk
Web: www.bankofengland.co.uk/museum
Dir: *museum housed in Bank of London, entrance in Bartholomew Lane. Bank underground, exit 2*
The museum tells the story of the Bank of England from its foundation in 1694 to its role in today's economy. Interactive programmes with graphics and video help explain its many roles. Unique collection of bank notes and a genuine gold bar, which may be handled.
Times: *Open all year, Mon-Fri 10-5. Closed wknds & BHs. Open on day of Lord Mayor's Show.
Facilities: ℗ (10 mins walk) ♿ (special need presentation, advance notice helpful), toilets for disabled, shop, audio commentaries available ⊗ (ex assist dogs) 🚌 (no parking)

LONDON EC4
Middle Temple Hall
The Temple, EC4Y 9AT
☎ 020 7427 4800 & 4820
🖷 020 7427 4801
e-mail: banqueting@middletemple.org.uk
Web: www.middletemple.org.uk
Dir: *Underground - Temple, Blackfriars. Turn left at the embankment & left into Middle Temple Lane. Hall half way up on left*
Between Fleet Street and the Thames are the Middle and Inner Temples, separate Inns of Court, so named after the Knights Templar who occupied the site from about 1160. Middle Temple Hall is a fine example of Tudor architecture and was completed in about 1570. The hall has a double hammerbeam roof and beautiful stained glass. The 29ft-long high table was made from a single oak tree.
Times: Open all year, Mon-Fri 10-12 & 3-4. Closed BH & legal vacations.
Facilities: ℗ (meters) 🍽 (licensed) ♿ toilets for disabled, shop, tours available ⊗ (ex assist dogs)

LONDON N7
Freightliners City Farm
Sheringham Road, Islington, N7 8PF
☎ 020 7609 0467
🖷 020 7609 9934
e-mail: robert@freightlinersfarm.org.uk
Web: www.freightlinersfarm.org.uk
Dir: *off Liverpool Rd*
A city farm bringing rural life into an urban setting. A variety of animals can be seen at the farm, including cows, pigs, goats, sheep and poultry. Some interesting building projects are taking place at the farm, including a strawbale building, solar dome, an outside bread oven and a continental beehive. A Saturday market offers organic produce, arts and crafts and much more.
Times: *Open Winter: 10-4. Summer: 10-4.45
Facilities: ℗ (charged) ℗ (20yds) (pay & display) ⊡ 🎋 ♿ toilets for disabled shop, garden centre, tours available ⊗ (ex assist dogs) 🚌

LONDON

LONDON

LONDON NW3

Kenwood House

Hampstead Lane, NW3 7JR

☎ 020 8348 1286

🖹 020 7973 3891

Web: www.english-heritage.org.uk

Dir: *Underground - Hampstead*

In splendid grounds beside Hampstead Heath, this outstanding neo-classical house contains one of the most important collections of paintings ever given to the nation. Works by Rembrandt, Vermeer, Turner, Gainsborough and Reynolds are all set against a backdrop of sumptuous rooms. Scenes from *Notting Hill* and *Mansfield Park* were filmed here.

Times: Open all year, Apr-Oct, daily 11-5; Nov-Mar, daily 11-4. Closed 24-26 Dec & 1 Jan.

Facilities: Ⓟ (limited) ☕ 🍽 (licensed) ⛩ ♿ toilets for disabled, shop 🚌 #

LONDON NW9

Royal Air Force Museum

Grahame Park Way, Hendon, NW9 5LL

☎ 020 8205 2266

🖹 020 8358 4981

e-mail: groups@rafmuseum.org

Web: www.rafmuseum.org

Dir: *within easy reach of the A5, A41, M1 and North Circular A406 roads. Tube on Northern Line to Colindale. Rail to Mill Hill Broadway station. Bus route 303 passes the door*

Soar through the history of aviation from the earliest balloon flights to the latest Eurofighter. World-class collection of aircraft and wartime memorabilia, a Battle of Britain sound and light show. Aeronauts Interactive Centre offers hands-on entertainment.

Times: Open daily 10-6. (Last admission 5.30). Closed 24-26 Dec & 1 Jan.

Facilities: Ⓟ Ⓟ (0.5m) (while museum is open) ☕ 🍽 (licensed) ♿ (lifts, ramps & wheelchairs available), toilets for disabled, shop, tours available 🚫 (ex assist dogs) 🚌 (pre-booking preferred)

LONDON SE1

Bankside Gallery

48 Hopton Street, SE1 9JH

☎ 020 7928 7521

🖹 020 7928 2820

e-mail: info@banksidegallery.com

Web: www.banksidegallery.com

Dir: *E of Blackfriars Bridge, South Bank of the Thames, adjacent to Tate Modern and the Millennium Bridge*

Bankside Gallery is the home of the Royal Watercolour Society (RWS) and the Royal Society of Painter-Printmakers (RE). A series of regularly changing exhibitions throughout the year displays the work of both societies.

Times: *Open daily during exhibitions, 11-6.

Facilities: Ⓟ ♿ shop, tours available ⊗ (ex assist dogs) 🚌 (notice required)

LONDON SE10

National Maritime Museum

Romney Rd, SE10 9NF

☎ 020 8312 6565

🖹 020 8312 6632

e-mail: bookings@nmm.ac.uk

Web: www.nmm.ac.uk

Dir: *central Greenwich*

Britain's seafaring history displayed in an impressive modern museum. Themes include exploration and discovery, Nelson, trade and empire, passenger shipping and luxury liners, maritime London, costume, art and the sea, and the future of the sea. There are interactive displays for children.

Times: *Open all year, daily 10-5 (10-6 Jul-Aug). Closed 24-26 Dec.

Facilities: Ⓟ (50 yds) (parking in Greenwich limited) 🍽 (licensed) 🚻 ♿ (wheelchairs, advisory service for hearing/sight impaired), toilets for disabled, shop, tours available, audio commentaries available ⊗ (assist dogs) 🚌

LONDON

LONDON

LONDON SE10
Royal Observatory Greenwich

Greenwich Park, Greenwich, SE10 9NF

☎ 020 8312 6565

📄 020 8312 6632

e-mail: bookings@nmm.ac.uk

Web: www.nmm.ac.uk

Dir: *off A2, Greenwich Park, enter from Blackheath Gate only*

Charles II founded the Royal Observatory in 1675 'for perfecting navigation and astronomy'. It stands at zero meridian longitude and is the original home of Greenwich Mean Time. It houses an extensive collection of historic timekeeping, astronomical and navigational instruments. New astronomy galleries and the Peter Harrison Planetarium.

Times: Open all year, daily 10-5 (10-6 Jul-Aug). Partial closures 31 Dec, 1 Jan and London Marathon day.

Facilities: 🅿 (charged) 🚻 ♿ (assistance on request) toilets for disabled, shop, tours available ⊗ 🚌

LONDON SE23
The Horniman Museum & Gardens

London Road, Forest Hill, SE23 3PQ

☎ 020 8699 1872

📄 020 8291 5506

e-mail: enquiry@horniman.ac.uk

Web: www.horniman.ac.uk

Dir: *on A205*

Founder Frederick Horniman, a tea merchant, gave the museum to the people of London in 1901. The collection covers the natural and cultural world with displays on Vanishing Birds and African Worlds, Britain's largest collection of musical instruments, and world cultures. Activities for all ages.

Times: *Open all year, daily 10.30-5.30. Closed 24-26 Dec. Gardens close at sunset.

Facilities: 🅿 (opposite museum) 🗜 🚻 ♿ (large print leaflets, induction loop) toilets for disabled (railings & lowered sink) shop, tours available ⊗ (ex assist dogs or in gardens) 🚌 (telephone in advance)

LONDON SE5
South London Gallery
65 Peckham Road, SE5 8UH

☎ 020 7703 6120 & 9799 (info)

▤ 020 7252 4730

e-mail: mail@southlondongallery.org

Web: www.southlondongallery.org

Dir: *from Vauxhall take A202 to Camberwell Green. Gallery halfway between Camberwell Green and Peckham*

The gallery presents up to eight exhibitions a year of cutting-edge contemporary art, and has established itself as South East London's premier venue for contemporary visual arts. The Gallery also aims to bring contemporary art of the highest standards to audiences in South London and to assist in the regeneration of the area by attracting audiences from across Britain and abroad.

Times: *Open Tue-Sun, 12-6. Closed Mon

Facilities: ℗ (on-street parking) ⊡ 🏠 ♿ (disabled access, induction loop) toilets for disabled ⊗ (ex assist dogs) 🚌 (telephone in advance)

LONDON SW1
Tate Britain
Millbank, SW1P 4RG

☎ 020 7887 8888 & rec info 8008

e-mail: information@tate.org.uk

Web: www.tate.org.uk

Dir: *Underground - Pimlico*

Tate Britain is the national gallery of British art from 1500 to the present day, from the Tudors to the Turner Prize. The gallery holds the greatest collection of British art in the world and is the world centre for the understanding and

enjoyment of British art. Tate Britain also has regular special exhibitions that reflect the history of British art, and numerous public events. See website for details.

Times: Open daily 10-5.50. Closed 24-26 Dec.

Facilities: ℗ (100yds) (metered parking) ⊡ 🍽 (licensed) 🏠 ♿ (wheelchairs on request, parking by prior arrangement), toilets for disabled, shop, tours available, audio commentaries available ⊗ (ex assist dogs) 🚌 (contact in advance)

LONDON

LONDON SW1
Westminster Cathedral
Victoria Street, SW1P 1QW
☎ 020 7798 9055
▤ 020 7798 9090
e-mail: barrypalmer@rcdow.org.uk
Web: www.westminstercathedral.org.uk
Dir: *300yds from Victoria Station*
Westminster Cathedral is a fascinating example of Victorian architecture. Designed in the Early Christian Byzantine style by John Francis Bentley, its strongly oriental appearance makes it very distinctive. The foundation stone was laid in 1895 but the interior decorations are not fully completed. The Campanile Bell Tower is 273ft high and has a four-sided viewing gallery with views over London. The lift is open daily 9am-5pm Mar-Nov but shut Mon-Wed from Dec-Feb.
Times: *Open all year, daily 7am-7pm.
Facilities: ℗ (0.25m) (2hr metered parking) ☻ & (all parts accessible except side chapels, loop system) shop, tours available ⊗ (ex assist dogs) 🚌

LONDON SW3
National Army Museum
Royal Hospital Road, Chelsea, SW3 4HT
☎ 020 7730 0717
▤ 020 7823 6573
e-mail: info@national-army-museum.ac.uk
Web: www.national-army-museum.ac.uk
Dir: *Underground - Sloane Square*
The museum offers a unique insight into the lives of Britain's soldiers, with displays including weapons, paintings, equipment, models, medals, and uniforms.
Times: *Open all year, daily 10-5.30. Closed Good Fri, May Day, 24-26 Dec & 1 Jan.
Facilities: ℗ ℗ (coach parking only if pre-booked) ☻ (licensed) & (wheelchair lift to access lower ground floor), toilets for disabled (one unisex toilet), shop, tours available, audio commentaries available ⊗ (ex assist dogs) 🚌 (advance booking for free parking & talk)

LONDON SW3
Royal Hospital Chelsea

Royal Hospital Road, SW3 4SR

☎ 020 7881 5204

🖷 020 7881 5463

e-mail: info@chelsea-pensioners.org.uk

Web: www.chelsea-pensioners.org.uk

Dir: *near Sloane Square, off A3216 & A3031*

Founded in 1682 by Charles II as a retreat for army veterans who had become unfit for duty, through injury or long service. The buildings were designed and built by Sir Christopher Wren, and then added to by Robert Adam and Sir John Soane. The hospital houses some 300 'In-Pensioners'. Visitors can stroll in the grounds and visit the Chapel, Great Hall and Museum.

Times: Open daily Mon-Sat, 10-12 & 2-4, Sun 2-4. (Museum closed Oct-Mar)

Facilities: ℗ (limited) 🚻 ♿ (induction loop in post office) toilets for disabled, shop, tours available ⊗ (ex staff & assist dogs) 🚌 (limit of 50 per group)

LONDON W1
The Wallace Collection

Hertford House, Manchester Square, W1U 3BN

☎ 020 7563 9500

🖷 020 7224 2155

e-mail: enquiries@wallacecollection.org

Web: www.wallacecollection.org

Dir: *Underground - Bond St, Baker St, Oxford Circus*

Outstanding collection of art. As well as an unrivalled representation of 18th-century French art, Hertford House is the home of Frans Hals' 'Laughing Cavalier' and paintings by Gainsborough, Rubens, Delacroix and Titian. It houses the largest collection of arms and armour outside the Tower of London.

Times: *Open all year, Mon-Sat 10-5, Sun 12-5. Closed Good Fri, May BH, 24-26 Dec & 1 Jan.

Facilities: ℗ (NCP & meters) (meters free on Sun) ⊑ 🍽 (licensed) 🚻 ♿ (lift, ramp, wheelchair available upon request), toilets for disabled, shop ⊗ (ex assist dogs) 🚌

LONDON

LONDON

LONDON W2

Serpentine Gallery

Kensington Gardens, W2 3XA

☎ 020 7402 6075

🖹 020 7402 4103

e-mail: varind@serpentinegallery.org

Web: www.serpentinegallery.org

Dir: *Underground - Knightsbridge, Lancaster Gate, South Kensington. Bus 9, 10, 12, 52, 94*

The Serpentine Gallery, named after the lake in Hyde Park, is situated in the heart of Kensington Gardens in a 1934 tea pavilion, and was founded in 1970 by the Arts Council of Great Britain. Today the Gallery attracts over 400,000 visitors a year and is one the best places in London for modern and contemporary art and architecture.

Times: *Open daily 10-6.

Facilities: ❷ (charged) 🍴 ♿ toilets for disabled, shop ⊗ (ex assist dogs) 🚌

LONDON W4

Hogarth's House

Hogarth Lane, Great West Road, W4 2QN

☎ 020 8994 6757

🖹 0845 456 2880

e-mail: info@cip.org.uk

Web: www.hounslow.info

Dir: *50yds W of Hogarth rdbt on Great West Road, A4*

This 18th-century house was the country home of artist William Hogarth (1697-1764) during the last 15 years of his life. The house contains displays on the artist's life, and many of his satirical engravings. The gardens contain Hogarth's famous mulberry tree.

Times: Open Apr-Oct, Tue-Fri 1-5, Sat-Sun 1-6; Nov-Mar, Tue-Fri 1-4, Sat-Sun 1-5. Closed Mon (ex BHs), Jan, Good Fri & 25-26 Dec.

Facilities: ℗ (25 & 50yds) (spaces marked in Axis Centre car park) ♿ (telephone in advance to confirm), toilets for disabled, shop ⊗ (ex assist dogs) 🚌 (must pre-book)

LONDON WC1
British Museum

Great Russell Street, WC1B 3DG

☎ 020 7323 8000

🖹 020 7323 8616

e-mail: information@thebritishmuseum.ac.uk

Web: www.thebritishmuseum.ac.uk

Dir: *Underground - Russell Sq, Tottenham Court Rd, Holborn*

The museum brings together astounding examples of universal heritage, for free. Discover the world through objects like the Aztec mosaics, the Rosetta Stone, El Anatsui's African textiles or the colossal Ramesses II.

Times: *Open all year, Gallery: Sat-Wed 10-5.30 & Thu-Fri 10-8.30. Great Court: Sun-Wed 9-6, Thu-Sat 9am-11pm. Closed Good Fri, 24-26 Dec & 1 Jan.

Facilities: ℗ (5 mins walk) 🚻 🍴 (licensed) 🚬 ♿ (parking by arrangement) toilets for disabled, shop, tours available, audio commentaries available ⊗ (ex guide /companion dogs) 🚌 (educational groups must book by phone)

LONDON WC1
Petrie Museum of Egyptian Archaeology

Malet Place, Univerity College London, WC1E 6BT

☎ 020 7679 2884

🖹 020 7679 2886

e-mail: petrie.museum@ucl.ac.uk

Web: www.petrie.ucl.ac.uk

Dir: *1st floor, DMS Watson building, in Malet Place, off Torrington Place*

One of the largest and most inspiring collections of Egyptian archaeology anywhere in the world. The displays illustrate life in the Nile Valley from prehistory, through the era of the Pharoahs to Roman and Islamic times. Noted collection of the personal items that illustrate life and death in Ancient Egypt, including the world's earliest surviving dress.

Times: *Open all year, Tue-Fri 1-5, Sat 10-1. Closed for 1 wk at Xmas/Etr.

Facilities: (meters) ♿ (wheelchair lift), toilets for disabled, shop, tours available ⊗ (ex assist dogs) 🚌 (max 50 people)

LONDON

LONDON WC2

Hunterian Museum

The Royal College of Surgeons, 35-43
Lincoln's Inn Fields, WC2A 3PE

☎ 020 7869 6560

🖹 020 7869 6564

e-mail: museums@rcseng.ac.uk

Web: www.rcseng.ac.uk

Dir: *Underground - Holborn*

The Hunterian Museum at the Royal College
of Surgeons houses over 3000 anatomical
and pathological preparations collected by the
surgeon John Hunter (1728-1793). Displays
explore Hunter's life and work, the history of
the Hunterian Museum and the College, and
the development of surgery from the 18th
century to the present.

Times: Open all year Tue-Sat 10-5. Closed
21 Dec-3 Jan, Good Fri & Etr Sat.

Facilities: Ⓟ (15yds) (pay & display
8.30-6.30pm) ♿ (Descriptive tours by
arrangement), toilets for disabled, shop,
tours available ⊗ (ex assist dogs) 🚌 (must
pre-book)

BEXLEY

Hall Place

Bourne Road, DA5 1PQ

☎ 01322 526574

🖹 01322 522921

Web: www.hallplace.com

Dir: *near junct of A2 & A233*

Hall Place is an attractive Grade I listed
mansion of chequered flint and brick, with
wonderful gardens. There is topiary in the
form of the 'Queen's Beasts'; rose, rock, peat
and water gardens; and a herb garden with
plants (labelled in Braille) for medicine and
cooking. There is also a conservatory, a local
studies centre and museum. Telephone for
details of exhibitions, lectures and concerts.

Times: *Open all year, House: Mon-Sat
10-5, Sun & BHs 11-5 (Apr-Oct); Tue-Sat
10-4.15 (Nov-Mar). Gardens: Mon-Fri 7.30-
dusk, Sat & Sun 9-dusk.

Facilities: ❾ Ⓟ (100yds) (coaches park in
additional parking) ⌑ 🍽 (licensed) ♿ toilets
for disabled, shop, garden centre
⊗ (ex assist dogs) 🚌

KEW

The National Archives

Ruskin Avenue, TW9 4DU

☎ 020 8392 5202 & 020 8487 9202

🖷 020 8487 9202

e-mail: events@pro.gov.uk

Web: www.pro.gov.uk

Dir: *Underground - Kew Gardens*

The National Archives houses one of the finest, most complete archives in Europe, comprising the records of the central government and law courts from the Norman Conquest to the present century. It is a mine of information and with some interesting material, including the Domesday Book.

Times: *Open Mon, Wed & Fri, 9-4.45; Tue, 10-7; Thu, 9-7. Closed 1st wk in Dec, Sun & public holiday wknds.

Facilities: ❷ ⓟ (100yds) ☲ ♿ (hearing loops & large print text in museum) toilets for disabled shop ⊗ (ex assist dogs) 🚌 (advanced booking required)

MORDEN

Morden Hall Park

Morden Hall Road, SM4 5JD

☎ 020 8417 8091

🖷 020 8687 0094

e-mail: mordenhallpark@nationaltrust.org.uk

Web: www.nationaltrust.org.uk

Dir: *A298 (Bushey Rd), right at 2nd lights into Martin Way. Morden Hall signed*

A green oasis in the heart of South West London. A former deer park, with a network of waterways including meadow, wetland and woodland habitats. Also discover the picturesque rose garden with over 2000 roses, fragrant from May to September.

Times: Open daily, 8-6.

Facilities: ❷ ☲ 🍽 ⌱ ♿ (wheelchair, Braille guides, large handled cutlery), toilets for disabled, shop, garden centre, tours available 🚌 (pre-booking required) ✍

GREATER LONDON

GREATER LONDON/MERSEYSIDE

TWICKENHAM
Orleans House Gallery

Riverside, TW1 3DJ

☎ 020 8831 6000

🖷 020 8744 0501

e-mail: m.denovellis@richmond.gov.uk

Web: www.richmond.gov.uk

Dir: *Richmond road (A305), Orleans Rd is on right just past Orleans Park School*

Stroll beside the Thames and through the woodland gardens of Orleans House, where you will find stunning 18th-century interior design and an excellent public art gallery. Visitors can try out their own artistic talents in pre-booked workshops. Exhibitions throughout the year.

Times: *Open Oct-Mar, Tue-Sat 1-4.30, Sun & BHs 2-4.30; Apr-Sep Tue-Sat 1-5.30, Sun & BHs 2-5.30.

Facilities: ❷ ℗ (surrounding areas) (coach space not currently available) ᴦ & (handling objects & large print labels for some exhibitions), toilets for disabled, shop ⊗ (ex assist dogs) 🚌 (booking preferred)

LIVERPOOL
Central Library

William Brown Street, L3 8EW

☎ 0151 233 5858

🖷 0151 233 5886

e-mail: refhum.central.library@liverpool.gov.uk

Web: www.liverpool.gov.uk

Dir: *located between museum and art gallery*

The Picton, Hornby and Brown buildings, situated in the Victorian grandeur of William Brown Street, house Liverpool's collection of over one million books, forming one of Britain's largest and oldest public libraries. The Liverpool Record Office is one of the country's largest and most significant County Record offices. Regular exhibitions of treasures from collections, phone for details.

Times: *Open all year, Mon-Fri 9-6, Sat 10-4 & Sun 12-4. Closed BHs.

Facilities: ℗ (50yds) (pay & display parking only) & (lift, text magnification, reading machine), toilets for disabled (ask at control desk for key), tours available ⊗ (ex assist dogs) 🚌

LIVERPOOL
Sudley House

Mossley Hill Road, L18 8BX

☎ 0151 724 3245

e-mail: sudley@liverpoolmuseums.org.uk

Web: www.sudleyhouse.org.uk

Dir: *near Aigburth Station and Mossley Hill Station*

The former family home of the Liverpool merchant George Holt in the Liverpool suburb of Mossley Hill. Works on show are drawn mainly from his collection of British paintings including Landseer, Turner, Gainsborough, Reynolds and Romney as well as major pre-Raphaelite painters. Many of the original Victorian features of the building survive, including tiles, ceramics, stained glass and wallpaper.

Times: *Open Mon-Sat 10-5, Sun noon-5. Closed 23-26 Dec & 1 Jan.

Facilities: ❶ ⛾ ♿ ⊗ (ex assist dogs) 🚌

LIVERPOOL
Walker Art Gallery

William Brown St, L3 8EL

☎ 0151 478 4199

🖹 0151 478 4390

Web: www.nmgm.org.uk

Dir: *follow brown and white signs*

For over 120 years, visitors have been surprised, charmed & moved by The Walker's world-famous collection including masterpieces by Rembrandt, Poussin, Rubens and Murillo. Newly refurbished galleries will display an exciting and varied programme of must see exhibitions.

Times: *Open Mon-Sat 10-5, Sun 12-5. Closed 23-26 Dec & 1 Jan.

Facilities: ❶ (charged) ⓟ (0.25m) ⛾ 🍽 ♿ (prior notice appreciated, wheelchair on request), toilets for disabled, shop ⊗ (ex assist dogs) 🚌

MERSEYSIDE

MERSEYSIDE

LIVERPOOL
Merseyside Maritime Museum
Albert Dock, L3 4AQ

☎ 0151 478 4499

📄 0151 478 4590

Web: www.liverpoolmuseums.org.uk

Dir: *entry into Dock from The Strand*

Set in the heart of Liverpool's magnificent waterfront, the Merseyside Maritime Museum offers a unique insight into the history of the great port of Liverpool, its ships and its people.

Times: *Open daily 10-5. Closed 23-26 Dec & 1 Jan.

Facilities: 🅿 🍴 (licensed) ♿ (lifts, wheelchairs, ramps, ex pilot boat & basement), toilets for disabled, shop ⊗ (ex assist dogs) 🚌

LIVERPOOL
HM Customs & Excise National Museum
Merseyside Maritime Museum, Albert Dock, L3 4AQ

☎ 0151 478 4499

📄 0151 478 4590

Web: www.nmgm.org.uk

Dir: *Albert Dock - follow brown signs*

Enter the exciting world of smuggle busting where everyday items reveal their hidden secrets. Find a fake, rummage for hidden goods and spot a suspect traveller. Look into the illustrious history of HM Customs & Excise, it's the longest battle in history and it's still going on today!

Times: *Open daily 10-5. Closed 23-26 Dec & 1 Jan.

Facilities: 🅿 🅿 (100yds) 🖥 🍴 (licensed) ♿ (restricted wheelchair access, no access to basement,) toilets for disabled, shop ⊗ (ex assist dogs) 🚌 (pre-booked)

LIVERPOOL
Conservation Centre

White Chapel, L1 6HZ

☎ 0151 478 4999

📄 0151 478 4990

Web: www.nmgm.org.uk

Dir: *follow brown tourist signs to Whitechapel*

Award winning centre, the only one of its kind, gives the public an insight into the world of museum and gallery conservation.

Times: *Mon-Sat 10-5, Sun 12-5. Closed 23-26 Dec & 1 Jan.

Facilities: 🅿 (charged) 🅿 ⊐ ♿ toilets for disabled, shop 🚫 (ex assist dogs) 🚌

LIVERPOOL
Liverpool Museum

William Brown Street, L3 8EN

☎ 0151 478 4393

e-mail: themuseum@liverpoolmuseums.org.uk

Web: www.liverpoolmuseum.org.uk

Dir: *in city centre next to St George's Hall and Lime St, follow brown signs*

One of Britain's most interesting museums, the Liverpool Museum has diverse collections ranging from the Amazonian rain forests to the mysteries of outer space. Special attractions include the award-winning hands-on Natural History Centre and the Planetarium.

Times: *Open Mon-Sat 10-5, Sun noon-5. Closed 23-26 Dec & 1 Jan.

Facilities: 🅿 ⊐ ♿ toilets for disabled, shop 🚫 (ex assist dogs) 🚌 (book in advance)

MERSEYSIDE

MERSEYSIDE

PORT SUNLIGHT
Lady Lever Art Gallery
Wirral, CH62 5EQ
☎ 0151 478 4136
▤ 0151 478 4140
e-mail: ladyleverartgallery@nmgm.org
Web: www.nmgm.org.uk
Dir: *Follow brown heritage signs*
The Lady Lever Art Gallery houses many world famous works of art, including Pre-Raphaelite masterpieces by Millais, Burne-Jones and Rossetti. Dramatic landscapes by the great British painters, Turner and Constable are also displayed alongside portraits by Gainsborough, Romney and Reynolds.
Times: *Open all year, Mon-Sat 10-5, Sun 12-5. Closed 23-26 Dec & 1 Jan.
Facilities: ℗ (charged) ℗ (0.25m) ☕ ♿ (prior notice appreciated, wheelchair on request), toilets for disabled ⊗ (ex assist dogs) 🚌

PRESCOT
Prescot Museum
34 Church Street, L34 3LA
☎ 0151 430 7787
▤ 0151 430 7219
e-mail: prescot.museum.dlcs@knowsley.gov.uk
Web: www.knowsley.gov.uk/leisure
Dir: *situated on corner of High St (A57) & Church St. Follow brown heritage signs*
Permanent exhibitions reflecting the local history of the area, including its important clock and watch-making heritage. There is a programme of special exhibitions, events and holiday activities, telephone for details.
Times: Open all year, Tue-Sat 10-5 (closed 1-2), Sun 2-5. Closed BHs. Mon by appointment
Facilities: ℗ (100 yds) ♿ (ramp to ground floor) shop ⊗ (ex assist dogs) 🚌

SOUTHPORT
Atkinson Art Gallery
Lord Street, PR8 1DH
☎ 01704 533133 ext 2110
🗎 0151 934 2110
e-mail: atkinson.gallery@leisure.sefton.gov.uk
Web: www.atkinson-gallery.co.uk
Dir: *next to Town Hall*

The gallery specialises in 19th- and 20th-century oil paintings, watercolours, drawings and prints, as well as 20th-century sculpture. Temporary exhibitions are shown regularly at the art gallery.

Times: Open all year, Tue-Thu 10-5, Fri 12-5, Sat 10-5, Sun 2-5. Closed Mon
Facilities: ℗ (next street) (pay & display) 🍽 (licensed) ♿ shop ⊗ (ex assist dogs) 🚌

BACONSTHORPE
Baconsthorpe Castle
NR25 6LN
☎ 01799 322399
Web: www.english-heritage.org.uk
Dir: *0.75m N of Baconsthorpe off unclass road, 3m E of Holt*

The remains of a 15th-century castle, built by Sir John Heydon during the Wars of the Roses. The exact date when the building was started is not known, since Sir John did not apply for the statutory royal licence necessary to construct a fortified house. In the 1560s, Sir John's grandson added the outer gatehouse, which was inhabited until the 1920s, when one of the turrets fell down. The remains of red brick and knapped flint are reflected in the lake, which partly embraces the castle as a moat.

Times: Open at any reasonable time.
Facilities: ℗ 🚌 ⌗

NORFOLK

BURGH CASTLE
Burgh Castle
Great Yarmouth, NR31 9PZ
Web: www.english-heritage.org.uk
Dir: *at far W end of Breydon Water on unclass road, 3m W of Great Yarmouth*
Burgh Castle was built in the 3rd century AD by the Romans, as one of a chain of forts along the Saxon Shore - the coast where Saxon invaders landed. Sections of the massive walls still stand.
Times: Open at any reasonable time.
Facilities: ⊗ 🚌

CAISTER-ON-SEA
Caister Roman Site
Web: www.english-heritage.org.uk
Dir: *3m N of Great Yarmouth*
The name Caister has Roman origins, and this was in fact a Roman naval base. The remains include the south gateway, a town wall built of flint with brick courses and part of what may have been a seamen's hostel.
Times: Open at any reasonable time.
Facilities: ⊗ 🚌

KING'S LYNN
King's Lynn Arts Centre

St George's Guildhall, 29 King Street, PE30 1HA

☎ 01553 765565

🖨 01553 762141

e-mail: entertainment_admin@west-norfolk.gov.uk

Web: www.kingslynnarts.co.uk

Dir: *located just off Tuesday Market Place in King Street, next to Globe Hotel*

Although it has been used for many purposes, the theatrical associations of this 15th-century Guildhall are strongest: Shakespeare himself is said to have performed here. A year round programme of film, performing and visual arts takes place. Contact box office on 01553 764864 for details.

Times: *Open Mon-Sat, 10-2. Closed show days, Sun, BHs, Good Fri & 24 Dec-1st Mon in Jan.

Facilities: Ⓟ (50yds) (pay & display) 🖵 🍽 (licensed) ♿ (hearing loop, ramp), tours available ⊗ 🚌 ✂

KING'S LYNN
African Violet Centre

Terrington St Clement, PE34 4PL

☎ 01553 828374

🖨 01553 828376

e-mail: info@africanvioletcentre.ltd.uk

Web: www.africanvioletcentre.ltd.uk

Dir: *situated beside A17 5m from King's Lynn and 3m from A47/A17 junct*

A warm and friendly welcome awaits you at the African Violet Centre. As a major plant specialist the centre offers a wide variety of plants for any enthusiast. Best known for their vast selection and display of African violets. The African Violet Centre is a winner of many Chelsea Gold Medals.

Times: *Open all year Mon-Sat 9-5, Sun 10-5. Closed Xmas & New Year.

Facilities: Ⓟ 🖵 ♿ (ramps & wide doors), toilets for disabled, shop, garden centre ⊗ (ex assist dogs) 🚌

NORFOLK

NORTH CREAKE
Creake Abbey
NR21 9LF
Web: www.english-heritage.org.uk
Dir: *off B1355*
The ruins of the church of an Augustinian abbey, later converted to an almshouse.
Times: Open at any reasonable time.
Facilities: ⊗ (ex dogs on leads) 🚌 ⛢

NORWICH
Sainsbury Centre for Visual Arts
University of East Anglia, NR4 7TJ
☎ 01603 593199
🖹 01603 591053
e-mail: scva@uea.ac.uk
Web: www.scva.ac.uk
Dir: *A47 bypass W towards Swaffham. 1st exit onto B1108, follow brown signs*
The collection of Sir Robert and Lady Sainsbury was given to the University in 1973. This outstanding collection is housed in two buildings designed by Norman Foster and combines modern Western art with fine and applied arts from Africa, the Pacific, the Americas, Asia, Egypt, Medieval Europe and the ancient Mediterranean.
Times: *Open Tue-Sun 10-5, Wed 10-8
Facilities: ❷ (charged) voucher must be obtained from reception ⫩ �🍽 (licensed) 🪑 ♿ (parking at main entrance, wheelchair available on loan), toilets for disabled (ramp access), shop ⊗ (assist dogs by arrangement) 🚌 (advance booking)

ST OLAVES
St Olave's Priory

Web: www.english-heritage.org.uk

Dir: *5.5m SW of Great Yarmouth on A143*

Remains of an Augustinian priory founded nearly 200 years after the death in 1030 of the patron saint of Norway, after whom it was named.

Times: Open at any reasonable time.

Facilities: 🚌 ♿

THETFORD
Thetford Priory

Web: www.english-heritage.org.uk

Dir: *on W side of Thetford near station*

A glimpse of medieval religious life before the dissolution of the monasteries. The Priory of Our Lady of Thetford belonged to the Order of Cluny, and was founded in 1103 by Roger Bigod, an old soldier and friend of William the Conqueror.

Times: Open all year at any reasonable time.

Facilities: 🚌 ♿

NORFOLK

NORFOLK

THETFORD
Thetford Warren Lodge
Web: www.english-heritage.org.uk
Dir: *2m W of Thetford, off B1107*

The remains of a two-storey hunting lodge, built in the 15th-century of flint with stone dressings.

Times: Open at any reasonable time.
Facilities: 🚌 ⛨

TITCHWELL
RSPB Nature Reserve
King's Lynn, PE31 8BB
☎ 01485 210779
🖨 01485 210779
e-mail: titchwell@rspb.org.uk
Web: rspb@org.uk
Dir: *6m E of Hunstanton on A149, signed entrance*

On the Norfolk coast, Titchwell Marsh is the RSPB's most visited reserve. Hundreds and thousands of migrating birds pass through in spring and autumn and many stay during winter, providing an opportunity to see many species of ducks, waders, seabirds and geese and also the RSPB emblem bird, the Avocet.

Times: Open at all times. Visitor Centre daily 9.30-5 (4 Nov-Mar).
Facilities: 🅿 (charged) 🖵 🍴 ♿ (ramps to hides, wheelchair bays in hides) toilets for disabled, shop, tours available
🚌 (advance booking essential)

WEETING

Weeting Castle

IP27 0RQ

Web: www.english-heritage.org.uk

Dir: *2m N of Brandon off B1106*

This ruined 11th-century fortified manor house stands in a moated enclosure. There are interesting but slight remains of a three-storey cross-wing.

Times: Open at any reasonable time.

Facilities: 🚌 ⌗

KETTERING

Alfred East Gallery

Sheep St, NN16 0AN

☎ 01536 534274

🖷 01536 534370

e-mail: museum@kettering.gov.uk

Web: www.kettering.gov.uk

Dir: *A43/A6, located in town centre, next to library*

The Gallery has a permanent exhibition space showing work by Sir Alfred East, Thomas Cooper Gotch and other local artists, as well as selections from the Gallery's contemporary collection. Two further display spaces are dedicated to monthly changing exhibitions of art, craft and photography by local artists. There is also a monthly lunchtime talks programme.

Times: *Open all year, Tue-Sat 9.30-5 (closed BHs)

Facilities: Ⓟ (300yds) 🚻 ♿ shop 🚫 (ex assist dogs) 🚌

NORTHAMPTONSHIRE/ NORTHUMBERLAND

NORTHAMPTON
Northampton Museum & Art Gallery
Guildhall Road, NN1 1DP
☎ 01604 838111
🖹 01604 838720
e-mail: museums@northampton.gov.uk
Web: www.northampton.gov.uk/museums
Dir: *in town centre, in Guildhall Rd*
Home to the world's largest collection of shoes, Northampton Museum and Art Gallery displays shoes that have been in fashion through the ages, from Ferragamo to Vivienne Westwood. Life and Sole tells the history of footware, and other displays detail the history of Northampton, and British and Oriental ceramics and glass.
Times: Open all year, Mon-Sat 10-5, Sun 2-5. (closed 25-26 Dec & 1 Jan)
Facilities: ℗ (200 yds) (car parks at bottom of Guildhall Rd) ♿ (wheelchairs available, large print catalogues), toilets for disabled on ground floor, shop, tours available, audio commentaries available
⊗ (ex assist dogs) 🚌 (pre-book)

CARRAWBROUGH
Temple of Mithras (Hadrian's Wall)
Web: www.english-heritage.org.uk
Dir: *3.75m W of Chollerford on B6318*
This fascinating Mithraic temple was uncovered by a farmer in 1949. Its three altars to the war god Mithras, date from the third century AD, and are now in the Museum of Antiquities in Newcastle, but there are copies on site.
Times: Open at any reasonable time.
Facilities: ℗ 🚌 ⚏

MORPETH

Morpeth Chantry Bagpipe Museum

Bridge Street, NE61 1PD

☎ 01670 500717

🖹 01670 500710

e-mail: anne.moore@castlemorpeth.gov.uk

Dir: *off A1 in Morpeth town centre*

This unusual museum specialises in the history and development of Northumbrian small pipes and their music. They are set in the context of bagpipes from around the world, from India to Inverness.

Times: Open all year, Mon-Sat, 10-5, open Sun in Aug & Dec. Closed 25-26 Dec, 1 Jan & Etr Mon.

Facilities: ℗ (100yds) ♿ (induction loop, large print text, DVD guide to museum,), shop, tours available, audio commentaries available 🚌

NORHAM

Norham Castle

TD15 2JY

☎ 01289 382329

Web: www.english-heritage.org.uk

A mighty border fortress built in 1160, this was one of the strongest of the border castles. Take an audio tour conjuring up four centuries of sieges and war with the Scots.

Times: Admission limited. Please call 01289 304493 for details.

Facilities: ℗ ♿ ⊗ 🚌 ♯

NORTHUMBERLAND

NOTTINGHAMSHIRE

EDWINSTOWE
Sherwood Forest Country Park & Visitor Centre
Mansfield, NG21 9HN
☎ 01623 823202 & 824490
🖹 01623 823202
e-mail: sherwood.forest@nottscc.gov.uk
Web: www.nottinghamshire.gov.uk/countryparks
Dir: *on B6034 N of Edwinstowe between A6075 and A616*

At the heart of the Robin Hood legend is Sherwood Forest. Today it is a country park and visitor centre with 450 acres of oaks and birches with waymarked pathways. A year-round programme of events includes the Robin Hood Festival, 30 Jul-5 Aug 2007.

Times: *Open all year. Country Park: open daily dawn to dusk. Visitor Centre: open daily 10-5 (4.30 Nov-Mar)

Facilities: ❶ (charged) Ⓟ (0.5m) (charges at certain times) ⌷ ⑴ (licensed) ⌒ ♿ (wheelchair and electric buggy loan), toilets for disabled (unisex for wheelchair users) shop 🚌

NEWARK-ON-TRENT
Newark Millgate Museum
48 Millgate, NG24 4TS
☎ 01636 655730
🖹 01636 655735
e-mail: museums@nsdc.info
Web: www.newark-sherwooddc.gov.uk
Dir: *easy access from A1 & A46*

The museum is home to diverse social collections and it features fascinating exhibitions - recreated streets, shops and houses in period settings. There are also children's activities. The mezzanine gallery, home to a number of temporary exhibitions shows the work of local artists, designers and photographers.

Times: Open Apr-Sep: Tue-Sun, 10.30-4.30, Oct-Mar: Tue-Sun, 10.30-4. Open spring and summer BH Mon, 10.30-4.

Facilities: Ⓟ (250yds) ⌷ ♿ toilets for disabled 1 w/chair toilet on ground floor, shop ⊗ (ex assist dogs) 🚌 (pre-book)

NOTTINGHAM
Green's Windmill

Windmill Lane, Sneinton, NG2 4QB

☎ 0115 915 6878

▤ 0115 915 6875

e-mail: info@greensmill.org.uk

Web: www.greensmill.org.uk

Dir: *off B686, 500yds from Ice Centre*

Restored to working order, take a look around the mill and see how grain is turned into flour by harnessing the power of the wind. Find out about the "mathematician miller" George Green and his theories, and test your mind with hands on puzzles and experiments. There's also a guinea pig piggery. 2007 is the bicentenary of the mill.

Times: Open all year Wed-Sun, 10-4, also BHs. Phone for Xmas & New Year closing.

Facilities: ❷ ℗ on road ⊼ ♿ (parking in Millyard,) toilets for disabled wide cubicles, hand rails, lever taps, shop, tours available ⊗ (ex assist dogs) 🚌 (pre-book only)

NOTTINGHAM
The Lace Centre

Severns Building, Castle Road, NG1 6AA

☎ 0115 941 3539

▤ 0115 941 3539

Dir: *follow signs for Castle, situated opposite Robin Hood statue*

Exquisite Nottingham lace fills this small 14th-century building to capacity, with panels also hanging from the beamed ceiling. There are weekly demonstrations of lace-making on Thursday afternoons from Easter to October. Telephone for details.

Times: Open all year. Jan-Mar, daily 10-4; Apr-Nov, 10-5. Every Sun 11-4. Closed Xmas & New Year

Facilities: ℗ (100yds) (metered street parking) shop 🚌

NOTTINGHAMSHIRE

NOTTINGHAMSHIRE/OXFORDSHIRE

OLLERTON
Rufford Abbey and Country Park
NG22 9DF
☎ 01623 822944
🖷 01623 824840
e-mail: rufford.park@nottscc.gov.uk
Web: www.nottinghamshire.gov.uk/countryparks
Dir: *2m S of Ollerton, adjacent to A614*

At the heart of the wooded country park stand the remains of a 12th-century Cistercian Abbey, housing an exhibition on the life of a Cistercian Monk at Rufford. There is wildlife on the lake; formal gardens with sculptures, and Britain's first centre for studio ceramics.

Times: *Open all year 10.30-5 (craft centre closes 3pm Jan & Feb). For further details of opening times telephone establishment. Closed 25 Dec.

Facilities: ℗ (charged) (charged for at various times of year) 🖵 ⏐◉⏐ (licensed) 🛱 ⅄ (lift to craft centre, w/chair and electric buggy loan), toilets for disabled (unisex), shop, garden centre 🚌

BANBURY
Banbury Museum
Spiceball Park Road, OX16 2PQ
☎ 01295 259855
🖷 01295 269469
e-mail: banburymuseum@cherwell-dc.gov.uk
Web: www.cherwell-dc.gov.uk/banburymuseum
Dir: *M40 junct 11 straight across at first rdbt into Hennef Way, left at next rdbt into Concord Ave, right at next rdbt & left at next rdbt, Castle Quay Shopping Centre & Museum on right*

Exciting displays telling of Banbury's origins and historic past. The Civil War; the plush manufacturing industry; the Victorian market town; costume from the 17th century to the present day; Tooley's Boatyard and the Oxford Canal, are some of the subjects illustrated.

Times: *Open all year, Mon-Sat, 10-5, Sun 10.30-4.30.

Facilities: ℗ (500yds) ⏐◉⏐ (licensed) ⅄ toilets for disabled, shop, tours available ⊗ (ex assist dogs) 🚌 (must pre-book)

DEDDINGTON
Deddington Castle

OX5 4TE

Web: www.english-heritage.org.uk

Dir: *S of B4031 on E side of Deddington*

The large earthworks of the outer and inner baileys can be seen; the remains of 12th-century castle buildings have been excavated, but they are not now visible.

Times: Open any reasonable time.

Facilities: 🚌 ⚞

MINSTER LOVELL
Minster Lovell Hall & Dovecot

OX8 5RN

Web: www.english-heritage.org.uk

Dir: *adjacent to Minster Lovell Church, 3m W of Witney off A40*

Home of the ill-fated Lovell family, the ruins of the 15th-century house are steeped in history and legend. One of the main features of the estate is the medieval dovecote.

Times: Open any reasonable time. Dovecote exterior only

Facilities: 🚌 ⚞

OXFORDSHIRE

OXFORDSHIRE

NORTH LEIGH
North Leigh Roman Villa
OX8 6QB
Web: www.english-heritage.org.uk
Dir: *2m N of North Leigh*

This is the remains of a large and well-built Roman courtyard villa. The most important feature is an almost complete mosaic tile floor, which is intricately patterned in reds and browns.

Times: Open, grounds all year. Viewing window for mosaic tile floor. Pedestrian access only from the main road - 600yds.

Facilities: ℗ 🚌 ♿

OXFORD
Museum of the History of Science
Old Ashmolean Building, Broad Street, OX1 3AZ
☎ 01865 277280
🖨 01865 277288
e-mail: museum@mhs.ox.ac.uk
Web: www.mhs.ox.ac.uk
Dir: *next to Sheldonian Theatre in city centre, on Broad St*

The first purpose built museum in Britain, containing the world's finest collection of early scientific instruments used in astronomy, navigation, surveying, physics and chemistry.

Times: *Open Tue-Sat 12-4, Sun 2-5. Closed Xmas and Etr Hols.

Facilities: ℗ (300yds) (limited street parking, meters) ♿ (lift), toilets for disabled, shop, tours available, audio commentaries available ⊗ (ex assist dogs) 🚌 (max 15 people, pre-book only)

OXFORD
St Edmund Hall

College of Oxford University, OX1 4AR

☎ 01865 279000

🖹 01865 279090

e-mail: bursary@seh.ox.ac.uk

Web: www.seh.ox.ac.uk

Dir: *Queen's Lane Oxford at end of High St*

This is the only surviving medieval academic hall and has a Norman crypt, 17th-century dining hall, chapel and quadrangle. Other buildings are of the 18th and 20th centuries.

Times: Open all year. Closed 24 Dec-4 Jan, 9-18 Apr & 28-31 Aug.

Facilities: ♋ ♿ toilets for disabled ⊗ (ex assist dogs) 🚌 (prior notice required)

OXFORD
Ashmolean Museum of Art & Archaeology

Beaumont Street, OX1 2PH

☎ 01865 278000

🖹 01865 278018

Web: www.ashmol.ox.ac.uk

Dir: *city centre, opposite The Randolph Hotel*

The oldest museum in the country, opened in 1683, the Ashmolean contains Oxford University's priceless collections. Many important historical art pieces and artefacts are on display, including work from Ancient Greece through to the 20th century.

Times: Open all year, Tue-Sat 10-5, Sun 12-5 BH Mons 10-5. Closed Etr & during St.Giles Fair in early Sep, Xmas & 1 Jan.

Facilities: ℗ (100-200yds) (pay & display) ♋ 🍽 (licensed) ♿ (entry ramp from Beaumont St. Tel. before visit) toilets for disabled, shop, tours available ⊗ 🚌 (big parties split 15 max, booking req)

OXFORDSHIRE

OXFORD
**Oxford University Museum of
Natural History**
Parks Road, OX1 3PW
☎ 01865 272950
🖹 01865 272970
e-mail: info@oum.ox.ac.uk
Web: www.oum.ox.ac.uk
Dir: *opposite Keble College*
Built between 1855 and 1860, this museum of "the natural sciences" was intended to satisfy a growing interest in biology, botany, archaeology, zoology, entomology and so on. The museum reflects Oxford University's position as a 19th-century centre of learning, with displays of early dinosaur discoveries, Darwinian evolution and Elias Ashmole's collection of preserved animals.
Times: Open daily 12-5. Times vary at Xmas & Etr.
Facilities: Ⓟ (200yds) (meter parking) 🚻 ♿ (lift access to gallery), toilets for disabled, shop ⊗ 🚌

OXFORD
Pitt Rivers Museum
South Parks Road, OX1 3PP
☎ 01865 270927
🖹 01865 270943
e-mail: prm@prm.ox.ac.uk
Web: www.prm.ox.ac.uk
Dir: *10 min walk from city centre, visitors' entrance on Parks Rd through Oxford Univiersity Museum of Natural History*
The museum is one of the city's most popular attractions. It is part of the University of Oxford and was founded in 1884. The collections held at the museum are internationally acclaimed, and contain many objects from different cultures of the world and from various periods.
Times: Open all year. Mon-Sun 12-4.30. Closed Xmas & Etr, open BHs.
Facilities: (parking for disabled if booked) ♿ (audio guide, wheelchair trail), toilets for disabled, shop, audio commentaries available ⊗ (ex assist dogs) 🚌

UFFINGTON
Uffington Castle, White Horse & Dragon Hill

☎ 01793 762209

Dir: *S of B4507*

The 'castle' is an Iron Age fort on the ancient Ridgeway Path. It covers about eight acres and has only one gateway. On the hill below the fort is the White Horse, a 375ft prehistoric figure carved in the chalk hillside and thought to be about 3000 years old.

Times: *Open at any reasonable time.

Facilities: ℗ (charged) ⊓ (disabled car park) 🚌 ☘

WOODSTOCK
The Oxfordshire Museum

Fletcher's House, Park Street, OX20 1SN

☎ 01993 811456

🖹 01993 813239

e-mail: oxon.museum@oxfordshire.go.uk

Web: www.oxfordshire.gov.uk/the_oxfordshire_museum

Dir: *A44 Evesham-Oxford, follow signs for Blenheim Palace. Museum opposite church*

Situated in the heart of the historic town of Woodstock, the award-winning redevelopment of Fletcher's House provides a home for the county museum which celebrates Oxfordshire in all its diversity. Collections of local history, art, archaeology, landscape and wildlife.

Times: Open all year, Tue-Sat 10-5, Sun 2-5. Closed Good Fri, 25-26 Dec & 1 Jan. Galleries closed on Mon, but open BH Mons, 2-5.

Facilities: ℗ (outside entrance) (free parking) ⊡ ⑩ (licensed) ⊓ ♿ (chair lifts to all galleries), toilets for disabled, adjacent to other public toilets, tours available ⊗ (ex assist dogs) 🚌 (pre-booked only)

OXFORDSHIRE

RUTLAND

OAKHAM
Oakham Castle

Catmos Street, LE15 6HW

☎ 01572 758440

🖷 01572 758445

e-mail: museum@rutland.gov.uk

Web: www.rutland.gov.uk/castle

Dir: *off Market Place*

An exceptionally fine Norman Great Hall of a 12th-century fortified manor house. Earthworks, walls and remains of an earlier motte can be seen along with medieval sculptures and unique presentation horse-shoes forfeited by peers of the realm and royalty to the Lord of the Manor. Licensed for Civil Marriages. Please enquire for details of the Oakham Festival.

Times: Open all year, Mon-Sat 10.30-5 (closed 1-1.30), Sun 2-4. Closed Good Fri & Xmas.

Facilities: Ⓟ (400yds) (disabled parking only by notification) ⅙ toilets for disabled, shop ⊗ (ex assist dogs) 🚌 (pre-booking preferred)

OAKHAM
Rutland County Museum

Catmos St, LE15 6HW

☎ 01572 758440

🖷 01572 758445

e-mail: museum@rutland.gov.uk

Web: www.rutland.gov.uk/museum

Dir: *on A6003, S of town centre*

Rutland County Museum is the perfect introduction to England's smallest county. The 'Welcome to Rutland' gallery is a guide to its history. The museum includes a shop and study area. On show in the 18th-century Riding School are displays of archaeology, history and an extensive rural life collection.

Times: Open all year, Mon-Sat 10.30-5, Sun 2-4. Closed Good Fri, Xmas & 1 Jan.

Facilities: Ⓟ (charged) Ⓟ (adjacent) (pay & display, free on Sun) ⅙ (induction loop in meeting room) toilets for disabled, shop ⊗ (ex assist dogs) 🚌 (pre-booking preferred)

ACTON BURNELL

Acton Burnell Castle

SY5 7PE

Web: www.english-heritage.org.uk

Dir: *in Acton Burnell on unclass road 8m S of Shrewsbury*

The warm red sandstone shell of a fortified 13th-century manor house. The site of the first parliament at which the commons were fully represented.

Times: Open at all reasonable times.

Facilities: ♿ 🚌 ⚏

BOSCOBEL

Whiteladies Priory

Web: www.english-heritage.org.uk

Dir: *1m SW of Boscobel House, off an unclass road between A41 and A5*

Only the ruins are left of this Augustinian nunnery, which dates from 1158 and was destroyed in the Civil War. After the Battle of Worcester Charles II hid here and in the nearby woods before going on to Boscobel House.

Times: Open Apr-Oct, daily 10-5. Closed Nov-Mar.

Facilities: 🚌 ⚏

SHROPSHIRE

SHROPSHIRE

LILLESHALL
Lilleshall Abbey
TF10 9HW
☎ 0121 625 6820
Web: www.english-heritage.org.uk
Dir: *off A518 on unclass road*

In the beautiful grounds of Lilleshall Hall, the now ruined Lilleshall Abbey was founded shortly before the middle of the 12th century and from the high west front visitors can look down the entire 228ft length of the abbey church.

Times: Open Apr-Sep, daily 10-5.
Facilities: 🚌 ♿

MORETON CORBET
Moreton Corbet Castle
Web: www.english-heritage.org.uk
Dir: *off B5063, in Moreton Corbet*

Inherited by the Corbets in 1235, who are thought to have remodelled the great keep, this castle may already have been standing for over 100 years. It was remodelled in the 16th century and then partially demolished to make way for a great Elizabethan mansion house. Although damaged in the civil war, the castle and mansion stand today as one of the most picturesque ruins of the Shropshire Marches.

Times: Open at any reasonable time
Facilities: 🅿 ♿ 🚌 ♿

OSWESTRY
Old Oswestry Hill Fort

Web: www.english-heritage.org.uk

Dir: *1m N of Oswestry, off an unclass road off A483*

An impressive Iron Age hill-fort of 68 acres, defended by a series of five ramparts, with an elaborate western entrance and unusual earth-work cisterns.

Times: Open at any reasonable time.

Facilities: 🚌 ♿

NUNNEY
Nunney Castle

Web: www.english-heritage.org.uk

Dir: *3.5m SW of Frome, off A361*

Built in 1373, and supposedly modelled on France's Bastille, this crenellated manor house has one of the deepest moats in England. It was ruined by Parliamentarian forces in the Civil War.

Times: Open at any reasonable time.

Facilities: ♿ 🚌 ♿

SHROPSHIRE/SOMERSET

SOMERSET

STOKE SUB HAMDON
Stoke sub Hamdon Priory

North Street, TA4 6QP

☎ 01935 823289

Web: www.nationaltrust.org.uk

Dir: *between A303 & A3088*

A complex of buildings, begun in the 14th century for the priests of the Chantry Chapel of St Nicholas (now destroyed).

Times: *Open 26 Mar-Oct, daily 10-6 or dusk if earlier.

Facilities: ℗ ⊗ (on road parking only) ☘

STREET
The Shoe Museum

C & J Clark Ltd, High Street, BA16 0YA

☎ 01458 842169

🖷 01458 442226

Dir: *A39 to Street, follow signs for Clarks Village*

The museum is in the oldest part of the shoe factory set up by Cyrus and James Clark in 1825. It contains shoes from Roman times to the present, as well as buckles, engravings, fashion plates, machinery, hand tools and advertising material.

Times: *Open all year, Mon-Fri 10-4.45. Closed 10 days over Xmas and BHs.

Facilities: ℗ At Clarks Village ♿ (access wkdays only) shop ⊗ (ex assist dogs) 🚍

HALFPENNY GREEN
Halfpenny Green Vineyards
Bobbington, DY7 5EP
☎ 01384 221122
🖷 01384 221101
e-mail: enquiries@halfpenny-green-vineyards.co.uk
Web: www.halfpenny-green-vineyards.co.uk
Dir: *0.5m off B4176 Dudley to Telford road*

Using German, French and hybrid varieties that can prosper even in the poorest British summer, this vineyard offers 'The complete English wine experience.' This includes a self-guided vineyard trail as well as guided tours, wine-tasting, a craft centre and a visitor centre. Visitors can purchase wines with personalised labels for special occasions. Coarse fishing is also available.

Times: Open all year, daily 10.30-5.
Facilities: 🅿 ⬚ ⬚ (licensed) ⬚ toilets for disabled, shop, tours available ⊗ (ex assist dogs) 🚌 (by appointment)

LICHFIELD
Samuel Johnson Birthplace Museum
Breadmarket Street, WS13 6LG
☎ 01543 258441
🖷 01543 414779
e-mail: sjmuseum@lichfield.gov.uk
Web: www.lichfield.gov.uk/sjmuseum
Dir: *located in city centre market place*

Dr Samuel Johnson, author of the famous English dictionary of 1755, lexicographer, poet, critic, biographer and personality was born in this house in 1709. The birthplace now houses a museum dedicated to his life, work and personality. Five floors of exhibits featuring period room settings, introductory video and personal items owned by Johnson, his family and his famous friends.

Times: *Open daily Apr-Sep 10.30-4.30; Oct-Mar 12-4.30. (Last admission 4).
Facilities: 🅿 (500yds) ⬚ (large print text literature, induction loop system), shop, tours available ⊗ (ex assist dogs) 🚌 (prior booking preferred)

STAFFORDSHIRE

STAFFORDSHIRE

STAFFORD
Shire Hall Gallery
Market Square, ST16 2LD
☎ 01785 278345
🖹 02785 278327
e-mail: shirehallgallery@staffordshire.gov.uk
Web: www.staffordshire.gov.uk/sams
Dir: *M6 junct 13, follow signs to Stafford town centre then to gallery*
A fine gallery housed in the 18th-century Shire Hall - one of Staffordshire's most magnificent buildings. It holds exhibitions of contemporary arts, contains historic court-rooms and a Crafts Council selected craft shop.
Times: *Open all year Mon & Wed-Sat, 9.30-5; Tue 10-5; Sun 1-4. Gallery closes for exhibition changes and at BHs, please call for further details.
Facilities: ℗ (5 mins walk) 🚻 🍴 ♿ (Wheelchair lifts to some areas of the building) toilets for disabled, shop, tours available ⊗ (ex assist dogs) 🚌

STOKE-ON-TRENT
The Potteries Museum & Art Gallery
Bethesda Street, Hanley, ST1 3DW
☎ 01782 232323
🖹 01782 232500
e-mail: museums@stoke.gov.uk
Web: www.stoke.gov.uk/museums
Dir: *M6 junct 15/16 take A500 to Stoke-on-Trent. Follow signs for city centre (Hanley), Cultural Quarter & The Potteries Museum*
The history of the Potteries under one roof, including a dazzling display of the world's finest collection of Staffordshire ceramics. Other displays of natural, local and archaeological history, and a Mark 16 Spitfire commemorating its locally born designer - Reginald Mitchell.
Times: *Open Mar-Oct, Mon-Sat 10-5, Sun 2-5; Nov-Feb, Mon-Sat 10-4, Sun 1-4. Closed 25 Dec-1 Jan.
Facilities: ❷ (charged) ℗ (200yds) (park & ride 500yds away) 🚻 ♿ (lift, induction loop, 2 wheelchairs available) toilets for disabled, shop ⊗ (ex assist dogs) 🚌

FLIXTON

Norfolk & Suffolk Aviation Museum

Buckeroo Way, The Street, Bungay, NR35 1NZ

☎ 01986 896644

e-mail: nsam.flixton@virgin.net

Web: www.aviationmuseum.net

Dir: *off A143, take B1062, 2m W of Bungay*

Situated in the Waveney Valley, the museum has over 50 historic aircraft. Also Bloodhound surface-to-air missile, the 446th Bomb Group Museum, RAF Bomber Command Museum, the Royal Observer Corps Museum, RAF Air-Sea Rescue and Coastal Command and a souvenir shop. Among the displays are Decoy Sites and Wartime Deception, Fallen Eagles - Wartime Luftwaffe Crashes.

Times: Open Apr-Oct, Sun-Thu 10-5 (last admission 4); Nov-Mar, Tue, Wed & Sun 10-4 (last admission 3). Closed late Dec-early Jan.

Facilities: ❷ ℗ (100yds) ⊊ ㅈ & , (helper advised, ramps/paths to all buildings), toilets for disabled, shop 🚌 (advance booking preferred)

IPSWICH

Christchurch Mansion

Soane Street, IP4 2BE

☎ 01473 433554 & 213761

▤ 01473 433564

e-mail: christchurch.mansion@ipswich.gov.uk

Web: www.ipswich.gov.uk

Dir: *S side of Christchurch Park, close to town centre*

The house was built in 1548 on the site of an Augustinian priory. Set in a beautiful park, it displays period rooms and an art gallery which has changing exhibitions. The Suffolk Artists' Gallery has a collection of paintings by Constable and Gainsborough.

Times: *Open all year, Tue-Sat 10-5 (dusk in winter), Sun 12-4.30 (dusk in winter). Closed Good Fri, 24-26 Dec & 1-2 Jan. Open BH Mon.

Facilities: ℗ (10 min walk) ⊊ (licensed) & (tape guide for partially sighted) disabled toilet on ground floor, shop, tours available ⊗ 🚌

SUFFOLK

SUFFOLK

IPSWICH

Ipswich Museum

High St, IP1 3QH

☎ 01473 433550

🖨 01473 433558

e-mail: museum.service@ipswich.gov.uk

Dir: *follow tourist signs to Crown St car park. Museum 3 mins walk*

The Museum has sections on Victorian Natural History, Suffolk wildlife, Suffolk geology, Roman Suffolk, Anglo-Saxon Ipswich and Peoples of the World. There is also one of the best bird collections in the country.

Times: *Open all year, Tue-Sat 10-5. Closed Sun, BHs, 24-26 Dec & 1 Jan.

Facilities: Ⓟ (3 min walk) ♿ (lift), toilets for disabled, shop ⊗ (ex assist dogs) 🚌 (telephone in advance)

LEISTON

Leiston Abbey

IP16 4TB

☎ 01728 831354 & 832500

🖨 01728 832500

e-mail: admin@leistonabbey.co.uk

Web: www.leistonabbey.co.uk

Dir: *N of Leiston, off B1069*

For hundreds of years this 14th-century abbey was used as a farm and its church became a barn. A Georgian house, now used as a school for young musicians, was built into its fabric and remains of the choir, the church transepts and parts of the cloisters still stand.

Times: Open at any reasonable time.

Facilities: Ⓟ no overnight parking ♿ tours available ⊗ (ex on lead) 🚌

LINDSEY
Lindsey Chapel

Rose Green

Web: www.english-heritage.org.uk

Dir: *on unclass road 0.5m E of Rose Green*

Built mainly in the 13th century, this small thatched, flint-and-stone chapel incorporates some earlier work.

Times: Open all year, daily 10-4.

Facilities: ♿ ⊗ 🚌 ⚏

ASH VALE
Army Medical Services Museum

Keogh Barracks, Aldershot, GU12 5RQ

☎ 01252 868612

🖷 01252 868832

e-mail: armymedicalmuseum@btinternet.com

Web: www.ams-museum.org.uk

Dir: *M3 junct 4 on A331 to Mytchett then follow tourist signs*

The museum traces the history of Army medicine, nursing, dentistry and veterinary science from 1660 until the present day. See medical equipment and ambulances, including uniforms and medals.

Times: Open all year, Mon-Fri 10-3.30. Closed Xmas, New Year & BH. Wknds by appointment only.

Facilities: Ⓟ Ⓟ (300yds for coaches) ♿ (hand rails, wide doors, audio guide, braille guides) toilets for disabled (wide doors, emergency cord, hand rail), shop, tours available, audio commentaries available ⊗ (ex assist dogs) 🚌 (pre-booked only)

SUFFOLK/SURREY

SURREY/EAST SUSSEX

GUILDFORD
Guildford House Gallery

155 High Street, GU1 3AJ

☎ 01483 444740

🖷 01483 444742

e-mail: guildfordhouse@guildford.gov.uk

Web: www.guildfordhouse.co.uk

Dir: *N side of High St, opposite Sainsbury's*

An impressive building in its own right, Guildford House dates from 1660 and has been Guildford's art gallery since 1959. A changing selection from the Borough's Art Collection is on display, including pastel portraits by John Russell, topographical paintings and contemporary craftwork, as well as temporary exhibitions.

Times: Open Tue-Sat 10-4.45. Closed Good Fri, 25-26 Dec.

Facilities: ℗ (100yds) ⊇ ⍥ ⓑ (ramps available for w/chair access to ground floor), shop, tours available ⊗ (ex assist dogs) ⛟ (pre-book only)

BRIGHTON
Booth Museum of Natural History

194 Dyke Road, BN1 5AA

☎ 01273 292777

🖷 01273 292778

e-mail: boothmuseum@brighton-hove.gov.uk

Web: www.virtualmuseum.info

Dir: *from A27 Brighton by pass, 1.5m NW of town centre, opposite Dyke Rd Park*

The museum was built in 1874 to house the bird collection of Edward Thomas Booth (1840-1890). His collection is still on display, but the museum has expanded considerably since Booth's day and now includes thousands of butterfly and insect specimens, geology galleries with fossils, rocks and local dinosaur bones, a magnificent collection of animal skeletons, and an interactive discovery gallery.

Times: Open all year, Mon-Sat (ex Thu) 10-5, Sun 2-5. Closed Good Fri, Xmas & 1 Jan.

Facilities: ℗ (road opposite) (2 hr limit) ⓑ toilets for disabled, shop ⊗ (ex assist dogs) ⛟ (booking preferred)

BRIGHTON
Brighton Museum & Art Gallery
Royal Pavilion Gardens, BN1 1EE

☎ 01273 290900

🖹 01273 292841

e-mail: museums@brighton-hove.gov.uk

Web: www.brighton.virtualmuseum.info

Dir: *A23/M23 from London. In city centre near seafront. New entrance in Royal Pavilion Gardens*

A £10 million redevelopment has transformed Brighton museum into a state-of-the-art attraction. Innovative new galleries, including fashion, 20th-century design and world art, featuring interactive displays appealing to all ages. The museum has a spacious entrance located in the Royal Pavilion gardens.

Times: Open Tue-Sat 10-5, Sun 2-5. (Closed Mon ex BHs).

Facilities: ⓟ (5 mins walk) (Church St NCP & on street) ⏛ ⏱ (lift, tactile exhibits, induction loops, ramps), toilets for disabled, shop ⊗ (ex assist dogs) 🚍 (call in advance)

HASTINGS & ST LEONARDS
Old Town Hall Museum of Local History
Old Town Hall, High St, TN34 3EW

☎ 01424 781166

e-mail: oldtownmuseum@hastings.gov.uk

Web: www.hmag.org.uk

Dir: *off A259 coast road into High St. Signed*

Situated in the heart of Hastings Old Town, the museum was originally a Georgian Town Hall built in 1823. Refurbished displays tell the story of Hastings Old Town as a walk back in time, with features including a Cinque Ports ship, and interactive displays.

Times: *Winter: Oct-Mar, Mon-Fri 10-4 Sat-Sun 11-4. Summer: Apr-Sep Mon-Sat 10-5 Sun 11-5.

Facilities: ⓟ (150yds) (parking meters in operation) ⏱ (lift, evac chair, low-level displays, audio tour), toilets for disabled, shop, audio commentaries available ⊗ (ex assist dogs) 🚍

EAST SUSSEX

HERSTMONCEUX
The Truggery

Coopers Croft, BN27 1QL

☎ 01323 832355

📄 01323 832314

e-mail: sarah@truggery.fsnet.co.uk

Web: www.truggery.co.uk

Dir: *from A22 at Hailsham, Boship rdbt, take A271 towards Bexhill for 4m*

The art of Sussex trug making can be seen through all the work processes including preparing timber, use of the draw knife and assembly of trug.

Times: Open all year. Mon-Fri 10-5, Sat 10-1. Closed Sun. Jan-Apr opening times may vary.

Facilities: 🅿 ℗ (100yds) (limited parking on site) ⏩ shop, tours available 🚌 (up to 25 pre-arranged)

BRAMBER
Bramber Castle

BN4 3FB

Web: www.english-heritage.org.uk

Dir: *on W side of village off A283*

The remains of a Norman motte and bailey castle. The gatehouse, still standing almost to its original height, and walls are still visible.

Times: Open any reasonable time.

Facilities: 🅿 (limited parking) 🚌 🌿

CHICHESTER
Chichester Cathedral

West Street, PO19 1PX

☎ 01243 782595

📄 01243 812499

e-mail: visitors@chichestercathedral.org.uk

Web: www.chichestercathedral.org.uk

Dir: *in city centre*

The beauty of the 900-year-old cathedral, site of the shrine of St Richard, is enhanced by many art treasures, ancient and modern.

Times: Open end Mar-end Sep daily 7.15-7; end Sep-end Mar 7.15-6.

Facilities: ℗ (within city walls) 🍽️ (licensed) ♿ (touch & hearing centre, loop system) toilets for disabled, shop, tours available ⊗ (ex assist dogs) 🚌 (pre-booking preferred)

HIGHDOWN
Highdown Gardens

Highdown Gardens, Goring, BN12 6PE

☎ 01903 501054

📄 01903 218757

e-mail: chris.beardsley@worthing.gov.uk

Web: www.worthing.gov.uk/wbc

Dir: *N off A259 between Worthing & Littlehampton. Access off dual carriageway, from E proceed to rdbt*

Set on downland countryside this unique garden overlooks the sea, and has been deemed a national collection due to the unique assortment of rare plants and trees. It was the achievement of Sir Frederick and Lady Stern. Many of the original plants were collected in China and the Himalayas.

Times: *Open all year: Apr-Sep, Mon-Fri 10-6. Winter: Oct-Nov & Feb-Mar, Mon-Fri, 10-4.30; Dec-Jan, 10-4.

Facilities: ℗ (coaches by appointment only) 🪑♿ toilets for disabled (Radar key) ⊗ (ex assist dogs) 🚌 (by appointment only)

WEST SUSSEX

TYNE & WEAR

GATESHEAD
The Baltic Centre for Contemporary Art

South Shore Road, Gateshead Quays, NE8 3BA

☎ 0191 478 1810 & 440 4944

▤ 0191 478 1922

e-mail: info@balticmill.com

Web: www.balticmill.com

Dir: *follow signs for Quayside, Millennium Bridge. 15 mins' walk from Gateshead Metro & Newcastle Central Station*

Once a 1950s grain warehouse, part of the old Baltic Flour Mills, this international centre presents a dynamic programme of exhibitions and events. It consists of five art spaces, cinema, auditorium, library and archive, eating areas and shop. Check website for events.

Times: *Please see website for details

Facilities: ℗ (charged) ℗ 0.25 mile ☐ ⒩ (licensed) ㅄ ♿ (wheelchairs/scooters, Braille/large-print guides), toilets for disabled, shop, tours available ⊗ (ex assist dogs) 🚌

NEWCASTLE UPON TYNE
Museum of Antiquities

The University, NE1 7RU

☎ 0191 222 7849

▤ 0191 222 8561

e-mail: m.o.antiquities@ncl.ac.uk

Web: www.ncl.ac.uk/antiquities

Dir: *Situated on main campus of Newcastle University between The Haymarket & Queen Victoria Rd*

Artefacts from north east England from prehistoric times to AD 1600 are on display here. The principal museum for Hadrian's Wall, this collection includes models of the wall, life-size Roman soldiers and a newly refurbished reconstruction of the Temple of Mithras.

Times: Open all year, daily (ex Sun), 10-5. Closed Good Fri, 24-26 Dec & 1 Jan.

Facilities: ℗ (400yds) ㅄ ♿ (large print guide), shop, tours available ⊗ (ex assist dogs) 🚌

SUNDERLAND

Sunderland Museum & Winter Gardens

Burdon Rd, SR1 1PP

☎ 0191 553 2323

🖹 0191 553 7828

e-mail: sunderland@twmuseums.org.uk

Web: www.twmuseums.org.uk/sunderland

Dir: *in city centre on Burdon Rd, short walk from Sunderland metro and mainline stations*

Wide-ranging displays and many hands-on exhibits that cover the archaeology and geology of Sunderland, the coal mines and shipyards and the spectacular glass and pottery made on Wearside. Other galleries show the lifestyles of Sunderland women over the past century, and works by LS Lowry.

Times: Open all year, Mon-Sat 10-5, Sun 2-5.

Facilities: Ⓟ (150 yds) ☕ 🍽 (licensed) ♿ (lifts, induction loops), toilets for disabled, accessible toilets on all floors, shop, audio commentaries available 🚫 (ex assist dogs) 🚌 (pre-booking preferred)

RUGBY

The Webb Ellis Rugby Football Museum

5 Saint Matthew's Street, CV21 3BY

☎ 01788 567777

🖹 01788 537400

e-mail: service@webb-ellis.co.uk

Web: www.webb-ellis.co.uk

Dir: *on A428 opposite Rugby School*

An intriguing collection of Rugby football memorabilia is housed in the shop in which rugby balls have been made since 1842. Visitors can watch a craftsman at work, hand-stitching the footballs. Situated near to Rugby School and its famous playing field.

Times: *Open all year, Mon-Sat 9-5. Phone for holiday opening times.

Facilities: Ⓟ (500yds) ♿ shop 🚫 (ex assist dogs) 🚌 (for comfort, max 30 at one time)

WARWICKSHIRE/WEST MIDLANDS

WARWICK

Warwickshire Yeomanry Museum

The Court House Vaults, Jury Street
CV34 4EW

☎ 01926 492212

📄 01926 494837

e-mail: wtc.admin@btclick.com

Dir: *on corner of Jury St & Castle St, 2m E of M40 junct 1*

The vaults of the courthouse display militaria from the county Yeomanry, dating from 1794 to 1945. It includes regimental silver, paintings, uniforms and weapons. A small room in the cellars now houses the HUJ Gun project, a field gun captured by the Yeomanry in 1917.

Times: Open Etr-Oct, Sat-Sun & BHs, 10-1 & 2-4. Other times by prior arrangement.

Facilities: Ⓟ (300yds) (2hr max in nearby streets) shop ⊗

BIRMINGHAM

Aston Hall

Trinity Road, Aston, B6 6JD

☎ 0121 327 0062

📄 0121 327 7162

e-mail: bmag-enquiries@birmingham.gov.uk

Web: www.bmag.org.uk

Dir: *M6 junct 6 follow A38(M) Aston Expressway towards city centre. Leave at Aston Waterlinks and follow brown signs to Aston Hall*

Built by Sir Thomas Holte, Aston Hall is a fine Jacobean mansion complete with a panelled Long Gallery, balustraded staircase, and plaster friezes and ceilings. King Charles I spent a night here during the Civil War and the house was damaged by Parliamentary troops. It was also leased to James Watt Junior, the son of the great industrial pioneer.

Times: Open Etr-Oct, Tue-Sun 11.30-4. Closed Mon ex BHs.

Facilities: Ⓟ ⊡ ♿ (ground floor only partially accessible) shop ⊗ (ex assist dogs) 🚌 (by arrangement)

BIRMINGHAM
Blakesley Hall

Blakesley Rd, Yardley, B25 8RN

☎ 0121 464 2193

🖷 0121 464 0400

e-mail: laura_r_cox@birmingham.gov.uk

Web: www.bmag.org.uk

Dir: *A4040 onto Blakesley Rd, Hall 100yds on right*

Blakesley Hall is a fine Yeoman farmers' residence, built by Richard Smalbroke in 1590. It has a half-timbered exterior and a Stuart interior, with a wonderful herb garden. The visitor centre has a varied exhibition programme, tea room and gift shop. Regular weekend events take place throughout the open season.

Times: Open Apr-Oct, Tue-Sun & BHs, 11.30-4

Facilities: 🅿 ☕ 🍴 toilets for disabled, shop, tours available ⊗ 🚌 (book in advance)

BIRMINGHAM
Sarehole Mill

Cole Bank Road, Hall Green, B13 0BD

☎ 0121 777 6612

🖷 0121 303 2891

e-mail: bmag-enquiries@birmingham.gov.uk

Web: www.bmag.org.uk

Dir: *A34 towards Birmingham. After 5m turn left on B4146, attraction on left*

Home to Birmingham's only working water-mill; Sarehole Mill was built in the 1760s. Used for both flour production and metal rolling up to the last century, the Mill can still be seen in action during the summer months. Restored with financial backing from JRR Tolkien, who grew up in the area and cites Sarehole as an influence for writing *The Hobbit* and *Lord of the Rings*.

Times: Open Etr-Oct, Tue-Sun 11.30-4. (Closed Mon, ex BH Mon)

Facilities: 🅿 (no coaches) ⊗ (ex assist dogs) 🚌 (by arrangement)

WEST MIDLANDS

BIRMINGHAM
Birmingham Museum & Art Gallery
Chamberlain Sq, B3 3DH
☎ 0121 303 2834
🖹 0121 303 1394
e-mail: bmag-enquiries@birmingham.gov.uk
Web: www.bmag.org.uk
See one of the world's best collections of Pre-Raphaelite paintings here, including important works by Burne-Jones, a native of Birmingham. Also on display are fine silver, ceramics and glass. The archaeology section has prehistoric Egyptian, Greek and Roman antiquities, and also objects from the Near East, Mexico and Peru. New galleries explore the creation of art, while the Touch gallery includes talking sculptures, and Samurai armour. The Bull Ring explores the 800-year history of this well-known area.
Times: Open all year, Mon-Thu & Sat 10-5, Fri 10.30-5 and Sun 12.30-5.
Facilities: ℗ (carparks nearby) ☕ 🍴 (licensed) ♿ (lift), toilets for disabled, shop 🚫 🚌

BIRMINGHAM
Museum of the Jewellery Quarter
75-79 Vyse St, Hockley, B18 6HA
☎ 0121 554 3598
🖹 0121 554 9700
e-mail: bmag-enquiries@birmingham.gov.uk
Web: www.bmag.org.uk
Dir: *off A41 into Vyse St, museum on left after 1st side street*
This Museum tells the story of jewellery making in Birmingham from the Middle Ages right through to the present day. Enjoy a tour of an original jewellery factory, where the family firm of Smith and Pepper produced jewellery for over eighty years. This perfectly preserved 'time capsule' has changed little since the beginning of the 20th century.
Times: Open Etr-Oct, Tue-Sun 11.30-4. (Closed Mon ex BH Mon)
Facilities: ℗ (limited 2hr stay/pay & display) ☕ ♿ (tours for hearing/visually impaired booked in advance), toilets for disabled, shop 🚫 (ex assist dogs) 🚌 (pre-booked)

BIRMINGHAM
Soho House

Soho Avenue, Handsworth, B18 5LB

☎ 0121 554 9122

🖷 0121 554 5929

e-mail: bmag-enquiries@birmingham.gov.uk

Web: www.bmag.org.uk

Dir: *from city centre follow A41 to Soho Rd, follow brown heritage signs to Soho Ave*

Soho House was the elegant home of industrial pioneer Matthew Boulton between 1766 and 1809. Here, he met with some of the most important thinkers and scientists of his day. The house has been carefully restored and contains many of Boulton's possessions including furniture, clocks, silverware and the original dining table where the Lunar Society met.

Times: Open Etr-Oct, Tue-Sun 11.30-4. (Closed Mon ex BH Mons)

Facilities: ❷ ⬚ 🗙 🕭 (induction loop,) toilets for disabled, shop ⊗ (ex assist dogs) 🚌 (by arrangement)

BIRMINGHAM
RSPB Sandwell Valley Nature Reserve

20 Tanhouse Avenue, Great Barr, B43 5AG

☎ 0121 357 7395

🖷 0121 358 3013

Web: www.rspb.org.uk

Dir: *off B4167 Hamstead Rd into Tanhouse Ave*

Opened in 1983 on the site of an old colliery, Sandwell Valley is home to hundreds of bird, animal and insect species in five different habitats. Summer is the best time to see the yellow wagtails or reed warblers, while wintertime attracts goosanders, snipe, and redshanks. There are guided walks and bug hunts for the kids in summer, and a shop and visitor centre all year round.

Times: *Open Tue-Fri 9-5, Sat & Sun 10-5 (closes at dusk in winter). Closed Mon, 24 Dec-2 Jan

Facilities: ❷ Ⓟ 2km 🕭 🕭 all parts accessible, toilets for disabled, shop 🚌

WEST MIDLANDS

COVENTRY
Coventry Transport Museum
Millennium Place, Hales Street, CV1 1PN
☎ 024 7623 4270
🖷 024 7623 4284
e-mail: enquiries@transport-museum.com
Web: www.transport-museum.com
Dir: *just off junct 1, Coventry ring road, Tower St in city centre*

Coventry is the traditional home of the motor industry, and the museum's world-renowned collection displays over 150 years of its history. You can design your own car, feel what it's like to break the sound barrier at 763mph and even travel into the future.

Times: *Open all year, daily 10-5. Closed 24-26 Dec.

Facilities: ℗ (adjacent) (pay & display) ⌨ 💺 (audio tour, tactile floor & models, wheelchairs for hire), toilets for disabled, shop ⊗ (ex assist dogs) 🚌 (pre-booking preferred)

COVENTRY
St Mary's Guildhall
Bayley Lane, CV1 5QP
☎ 024 7683 2386
🖷 024 7622 0171
e-mail: info@theherbert.org
Web: www.theherbert.org
Dir: *in city centre near ruined cathedral*

This impressive medieval Guildhall has stood in the heart of Coventry for over 650 years, and has played its part in the history of the area. It served as Henry VI's court during the War of the Roses, was a prison to Mary, Queen of Scots, and was used as a setting by George Eliot in her novel *Adam Bede*. The Great Hall contains a Tournai tapestry commissioned for the visit of Henry VII and Queen Elizabeth in 1500.

Times: *Open Etr Sun-Sep, Sun-Thu 10-4

Facilities: ℗ (600yds) 🍽 💺 shop, tours available ⊗ (ex assist dogs) 🚌 (pre-booked)

COVENTRY

Herbert Art Gallery & Museum

Jordan Well, CV1 5QP

☎ 024 7683 2381 & 2565

📄 024 7683 2410

e-mail: artsandheritage@coventry.gov.uk

Web: www.coventrymuseum.org.uk

Dir: *in city centre near cathedral*

The Herbert is currently undergoing a major redevelopment, which is due for completion in 2008. During the time of the redevelopment there will be an active programme of temporary exhibitions, and plenty of events and activities for children.

Times: *Open all year, Mon-Sat 10-5.30, Sun 12-5. Closed 24-26, 31 Dec & 1 Jan

Facilities: ℗ (500yds) ⊑ ♿ (disabled parking, automatic doors), toilets for disabled (toilet on ground floor), shop ⊗ (ex guide/assistance dogs) 🚌 (pre-booking preferred)

COVENTRY

Jaguar Daimler Heritage Centre

Browns Lane, Allesley, CV5 9DR

☎ 024 7620 3322

📄 024 7620 2835

e-mail: jagtrust@jaguar.com

Web: www.jdht.com

Dir: *on A45, follow signs for Browns Lane Plant*

Established in 1983, the Jaguar-Daimler Heritage Trust maintains a unique collection of motor vehicles and artefacts manufactured by Jaguar Cars Ltd, and the many other renowned marques associated with the company.

Times: *Wkdays by appointment, no appointment required on last Sunday of the month.

Facilities: ℗ ⊑ ♿ ,toilets for disabled (1 toilet available on the ground floor) shop, tours available ⊗ (ex assist dogs) 🚌 (pre-book)

WEST MIDLANDS

COVENTRY
Priory Visitor Centre
Priory Row, CV1 5EX
☎ 024 7655 2242
🖷 024 7622 0171
e-mail: prioryvisitorscentre@coventry.gov.uk
Web: www.theherbert.org
Dir: *in city centre near cathedral*

Earl Leofric and his wife Lady Godiva founded a monastery in Coventry in the 11th century. This priory disappeared somewhere beneath the cathedral that was built on the site, until this cathedral was in turn demolished by Henry VIII in the 16th century. Soon after that most of the buildings on the site had been reduced to ground level, leaving modern archaeologists to discover the outlines of history. This visitor centre displays finds from the site as well as telling the story of Coventry's first cathedral.

Times: Open Mon-Sat 10-5.30, Sun noon-4
Facilities: Ⓟ (500yds) ᕐ toilets for disabled, shop Ⓧ (ex assist dogs) 🚌

DUDLEY
Museum & Art Gallery
St James's Road, DY1 1HU
☎ 01384 815575
🖷 01384 815576
e-mail: museum.pls@mbc.dudley.gov.uk
Web: www.dudley.gov.uk
Dir: *M5 N junct 2. Take A4123 signed to Dudley*

The museum houses the Brooke Robinson collection of 17th-, 18th- and 19th-century European painting, furniture, ceramics and enamels. A fine geological gallery, 'The Time Trail' has spectacular displays of fossils from the local Wenlock limestone and coal measures.

Times: *Open all year, Mon-Sat 10-4. Closed BHs.
Facilities: Ⓟ (25yds) ᕐ (Braille & large print text. Tactile objects) shop Ⓧ (ex assist dogs) 🚌 (pre-booking)

WEST MIDLANDS

KINGSWINFORD
Broadfield House Glass Museum
Compton Drive, DY6 9NS
☎ 01384 812745
e-mail: glass.museum@dudley.gov.uk
Web: www.glassmuseum.org.uk
Dir: *Off A491 Stourbridge to Wolverhampton road, just S of Kingswinford Village Centre*
Situated in the historic Stourbridge Glass Quarter, Broadfield House Glass Museum is one of the best glass museums in the world. Home to a magnificent collection of British glass from the 17th century to the present day, the museum hosts an exciting programme of exhibitions and events, and is a main venue for the International Festival of Glass, which is held in August. The museum also has a gift shop, and a hot glass studio.
Times: Open all year, Tue-Sun & BHs 12-4. Please phone for Xmas/Etr openings
Facilities: ℗ & toilets for disabled, shop, tours available ⊗ (ex assist dogs) 🚌

WALSALL
Walsall Leather Museum
Littleton Street West, WS2 8EQ
☎ 01922 721153
🖨 01922 725827
e-mail: leathermuseum@walsall.gov.uk
Web: www.walsall.gov.uk/leathermuseum
Dir: *On Walsall ring-road A4148 on N side of town*
Working museum in the saddlery and leather-goods 'capital' of Britain. Watch skilled craftsmen and women at work in this restored Victorian leather factory. Displays tell the story of Walsall's leatherworkers. Large shop stocks range of Walsall-made leathergoods.
Times: *Open all year, Tue-Sat 10-5 (Nov-Mar 4), Sun noon-5 (Nov-Mar 4). Open BH Mon. Closed 24-26 Dec, 1 Jan, Good Fri, Etr Sun & May Day.
Facilities: ℗ (10yds) ⊑ 🍴 & (staff with sign language skills,tactile activities, parking), toilets for disabled, shop, tours available ⊗ (ex assist dogs) 🚌 (max 60 people)

WALSALL

The New Art Gallery Walsall

Gallery Square, WS2 8LG

☎ 01922 654400

▤ 01922 654401

e-mail: info@artatwalsall.org.uk

Web: www.artatwalsall.org.uk

Dir: *signed from all major routes into town centre*

This exciting art gallery has at its core the Garman Ryan Collection, and a Children's Discovery Gallery that offers access to the very best in contemporary art in the only interactive art gallery designed especially for young people.

Times: *Open all year, Tue-Sat 10-5, Sun noon-5. Closed Mon ex BH Mon, 25-28 Dec & 1 Jan. Please telephone to confirm.

Facilities: ℗ (5 minutes on foot) (free on site for disabled) ⌑ (licensed) ⅗ (lift access to facilties, induction loop, large print), toilets for disabled, ground 1st and 4th floor, shop, tours available ⊗ (ex assist dogs) ▄▄

WOLVERHAMPTON

Bantock House and Park

Finchfield Road, WV3 9LQ

☎ 01902 552195

▤ 01902 552196

e-mail: bantockhouse@dial.pipex.com

Web: www.wolverhampton.gov.uk

Dir: *follow signs for Wolverhampton. Bantock House 1m out of city & well signed from ring road*

A rare survival of a Georgian farmhouse that was extended in the early 19th century. The current interior represents the Edwardian era. The ground floor is set out as the family home, while upstairs visitors can discover Wolverhampton's history. The gardens have been restored to their Edwardian designs.

Times: Open Apr-end Oct, 11-5; Nov-end Mar, 12-4. Closed Mon except BH

Facilities: ❷ ⌑ ⅌ ⅗ (wheelchair, induction loop, Braille guide) toilets for disabled, shop, tours available, audio commentaries available ⊗ (ex assist dogs) ▄▄ (please notify in advance)

BRADFORD-ON-AVON
Bradford-on-Avon Tithe Barn
Web: www.english-heritage.org.uk
Dir: *0.25m S of town centre, off B3109*

This impressive tithe barn, over 160ft long by 30ft wide, once belonged to Shaftesbury Abbey. The roof is of stone slates, supported outside by buttresses and inside by massive beams and a network of rafters.

Times: Open all year, daily 10.30-4. Closed 25 Dec.
Facilities: ℗ (charged) ♿ all parts accessible ⊗ 🚌 ⚏

LUDGERSHALL
Ludgershall Castle and Cross
SP11 9QR
Web: www.english-heritage.org.uk
Dir: *7m NW of Andover on A342*

Ruins of an early 12th-century royal hunting palace and medieval cross. The visitor can see large earthworks of the Norman motte-and-bailey castle and the flint walls of the later hunting palace. The stump of a medieval cross stands in the village street.

Times: Open at any reasonable time.
Facilities: ℗ (limited parking) ♿ 🚌 ⚏

WILTSHIRE

WILTSHIRE/WORCESTERSHIRE

WOODHENGE
Woodhenge

Web: www.english-heritage.org.uk

Dir: *1.5m N of Amesbury, off A345 just S of Durrington*

A Neolithic ceremonial monument dating from about 2300 BC, consisting of six concentric rings of timber posts, now marked by concrete piles. The long axis of the rings, which are oval, points to the rising sun on Midsummer Day.

Times: Open all reasonable times. Usual facilities may not apply around Summer Solstice 20-22 Jun. Please check.

Facilities: ℗ ♿ 🚌 �

WORCESTER
City Museum & Art Gallery

Foregate St, WR1 1DT

☎ 01905 25371

🖷 01905 616979

e-mail: artgalleryandmuseum@cityofworcester.gov.uk

Web: www.worcestercitymuseums.org.uk

Dir: *in city centre, 150m from Foregate St Train Station*

The gallery has temporary art exhibitions from both local and national sources. Museum exhibits cover geology, local and natural history. Of particular interest is a complete 19th-century chemist's shop. There are collections relating to the Worcestershire Regiment and the Worcestershire Yeomanry Cavalry.

Times: *Open all year, Mon-Fri 9.30-5.30, Sat 9.30-5. Closed Sun, 25-26 Dec, 1 Jan & Good Fri, Easter Mon and Whitsun BH Mon.

Facilities: ℗ (city centre) 🍽 ♿ (lift, induction loop), toilets for disabled, shop, tours available ⊗ 🚌 (pre-booking advised)

BURTON AGNES
Burton Agnes Manor House
Web: www.english-heritage.org.uk
Dir: *in Burton Agnes, 5m SW of Bridlington on A166*

A rare and well-preserved example of a Norman house. Some interesting Norman architectural features can still be seen, but the building was encased in brick during the 17th and 18th centuries. The house is near Burton Agnes Hall and the gardens are privately owned and not managed by English Heritage.
Times: Open Apr-Oct, daily 11-5.
Facilities: ⚏

KINGSTON UPON HULL
Maister House
160 High Street, HU1 1NL
☎ 01482 324114
🖹 01482 227003
Web: www.nationaltrust.org.uk
Dir: *city centre*

The house is a mid-18th-century rebuilding, notable for its splendid stone and wrought-iron staircase, ornate stucco work and finely carved doors. Only the staircase and entrance hall are open as the house is now let as offices.
Times: *Open all year, Mon-Fri 10-4 (Closed BH).
Facilities: Ⓟ ⊗ ♨

EAST RIDING OF YORKSHIRE

EAST RIDING OF YORKSHIRE

KINGSTON UPON HULL
Wilberforce House

23-25 High Street, HU1 1NE

☎ 01482 613902

🖹 01482 613710

e-mail: museums@hullcc.gov.uk

Web: www.hullcc.gov.uk/museums

Dir: *A63 from M62 or A1079 from York, follow signs for Old Town*

The early 17th-century Merchant's house was the birthplace of William Wilberforce, who became a leading campaigner against slavery. There are Jacobean and Georgian rooms and displays on Wilberforce and the anti-slavery campaign. The house also has secluded gardens. There are special exhibitions throughout the year.

Times: *Open all year, Mon-Sat 10-5 & Sun 1.30-4.30. Closed 25-26 Dec, 1 Jan & Good Fri.

Facilities: ⓟ (500yds) (meters on street) 🚻 ♿ (large print, video area & audio guides) shop ⊗ (ex assist dogs) 🚌 (prior booking)

KINGSTON UPON HULL
Maritime Museum

Queen Victoria Square, HU1 3DX

☎ 01482 613902

🖹 01482 613710

e-mail: museums@hullcc.gov.uk

Web: www.hullcc.gov.uk/museums

Dir: *A63 to town centre, museum is within pedestrian area*

Hull's maritime history is illustrated here, with displays on whales and whaling, ships and shipping, and other aspects of this Humber port. There is also a Victorian court room which is used for temporary exhibitions. The restored dock area, with its fine Victorian and Georgian buildings, is well worth exploring too.

Times: *Open all year, Mon-Sat 10-5 & Sun 1.30-4.30. Closed 25 Dec-2 Jan & Good Fri.

Facilities: ⓟ (100yds) ♿ all parts accessible, shop ⊗ (ex assist dogs) 🚌 (pre-booked only)

KINGSTON UPON HULL

'Streetlife' – Hull Museum of Transport

High Street, HU1 1PS

☎ 01482 613902

🖹 01482 613710

e-mail: museums@hullcc.gov.uk

Web: www.hullcc.gov.uk/museums

Dir: *A63 from M62, follow signs for Old Town*

This purpose-built museum uses a 'hands-on' approach to trace 200 years of transport history. With a vehicle collection of national importance, state-of-the-art animatronic displays and authentic scenarios, you can see Hull's Old Town brought vividly to life. The mail coach ride uses the very latest in computer technology to recreate a Victorian journey by four-in-hand.

Times: *Open all year, Mon-Sat 10-5, Sun 1.30-4.30. Closed 24-25 Dec & Good Fri

Facilities: ℗ (500yds) ⇰ ♿ all parts accessible, toilets for disabled, shop ⊗ (ex assist dogs) 🚌 (pre-booked only)

THORNTON

Thornton Abbey and Gatehouse

DN39 6TU

Dir: *7m SE of Humber Bridge, on road E of A1077*

This abbey, founded in 1139 for a community of Augustinian canons, was reconstructed from the 1260s as its prestige and riches grew. The remains of a beautiful octagonal chapter-house are notably fine. Most impressive is the 14th-century gatehouse, recognised as one of the grandest in England.

Times: Open Abbey Grounds: Apr-Sep, daily, 10-6; Oct-Mar, daily, 10-4. Gatehouse: Apr-Sep, 1st & 3rd Sun of month, 12-6; Oct-Mar, 3rd Sun of month 12-4.

Facilities: ℗ ♿ (mostly accessible apart from gatehouse) 🚌 ♯

EAST RIDING OF YORKSHIRE

NORTH YORKSHIRE

AYSGARTH
National Park Centre

Leyburn, DL8 3TH

☎ 01969 662910

🖷 01969 662919

e-mail: aysgarth@ytbtic.co.uk

Web: www.yorkshiredales.org.uk

Dir: *off A684, Leyburn to Hawes road at Falls junct, Palmer Flatt Hotel & continue down hill over river, centre 500yds on left*

A visitor centre for the Yorkshire Dales National Park, with maps, guides, walks and local information. Interactive displays explain the history and natural history of the area. Plan the day ahead with a light lunch in the coffee shop. Various guided walks begin here throughout the year.

Times: *Open Apr-Oct, daily 10-5; Winter open Fri-Sun, 10-4.

Facilities: ℗ (charged) ℗ (0.25m) ♨ ⏲ ♿ (viewing platform at Falls), toilets for disabled, shop ⊗ (ex assist dogs) 🚌 (by previous arrangement)

BEDALE
Bedale Museum

DL8 1AA

☎ 01677 423797

Dir: *on A684, 1.5m W of A1 at Leeming Bar. Opposite church, at N end of town*

Situated in a building dating back to the 17th-century, the Bedale is a fascinating museum. The central attraction is the Bedale fire engine, which dates back to 1742. Other artefacts include documents, toys, craft tools and household utensils, which all help to give an absorbing picture of the lifestyle of the times.

Times: Open all year Tue & Fri 10-12.30 & 2-4, Wed 2-4, Thu-Sat 10-12

Facilities: ℗ ℗ (20yds) (2hr disc, free long stay 400m) ♿ toilets for disabled, shop ⊗ (ex assist dogs) 🚌 (prior booking preferred)

DANBY

The Moors Centre

Lodge Lane, Whitby, YO21 2NB

☎ 01439 772737

▤ 01287 660308

e-mail: moorscentre@ytbtic.co.uk

Web: www.moors.uk.net

Dir: *turn S off A171, follow Moors Centre Danby signs . Left at crossroads in Danby and then 2m. Centre at bend on right*

The ideal place to start exploring the North York Moors National Park. There is an exhibition about the area as well as events, video, a shop and local walks. The Moors bus service operates from here - phone for details.

Times: Open all year, Apr-Oct, daily 10-5. Nov-Feb wknds only 11-4, Mar daily 11-4. Closed 25-26 Dec

Facilities: ❷ (charged per day ▭ ☷ ⅋ (woodland & garden trails, motorised & manual wheelchairs), toilets for disabled, located at tearoom, shop ⊗ (ex assist dogs & in grounds) ➡ (max 60 people)

EASBY

Easby Abbey

Web: www.english-heritage.org.uk

Dir: *1m SE of Richmond off B6271*

Set beside the River Swale, this Premonstratensian Abbey was founded in 1155 and dedicated to St Agatha. Extensive remains of the monks' domestic buildings can be seen.

Times: Open Apr-Sep, daily, 10-6; Oct, daily, 10-5; Nov-Mar, daily, 10-4. Closed 24-25 Dec. & 1 Jan

Facilities: ❷ ➡ ⌗

NORTH YORKSHIRE

FAIRBURN
RSPB Nature Reserve

Fairburn Ings, The Visitor Centre, Newton Lane, Castleford, WF10 2BH

☎ 01977 603796

e-mail: james.dean@rspb.org.uk

Dir: *W of A1, N of Ferrybridge. Signed from Allerton Bywater off A656. Signed Fairburn Village, off A1*

One-third of the 700-acre RSPB reserve is open water, and over 270 species of birds have been recorded. A visitor centre provides information, and there is an elevated board-walk, suitable for disabled visitors.

Times: *Access to the reserve via car park, open 9-dusk. Centre open 9.30-5 everyday. Car park open: 9-5. Closed 25-26 Dec.

Facilities: ❷ ㅈ ⟨ (raised boardwalk for wheelchair) toilets for disabled, shop ⊗ (ex assist dogs & in reserve) ▄▄▄ (booked one month in advance)

GRASSINGTON
National Park Centre

Hebden Road, BD23 5LB

☎ 01969 751690

🖹 01756 751699

e-mail: grassington@yorkshiredales.org.uk

Web: www.yorkshiredales.org.uk

Dir: *on B6265 in main Grassington car park*

The centre is a useful introduction to the Yorkshire Dales National Park. It has a video and a display on 'Wharfedale - Gateway to the Park', and maps, guides and local information are available. There is also a 24-hr public access information service through computer screens and a full tourist information service.

Times: Open Apr-Oct daily, 10-5; Nov-Mar, Fri, & Sat-Sun, 10-4 (also daily in school hols).

Facilities: ❷ (charged) ㅈ ⟨, toilets for disabled (radar key) shop, tours available ▄▄▄ (student groups 10 max at once)

MALHAM
Malham National Park Centre

Skipton, BD23 4DA

☎ 01969 652381

🖹 01969 652389

e-mail: malham@yorkshiredales.org.uk

Web: www.yorkshiredales.org.uk

Dir: *off A65 at Gargrave opposite petrol station. Malham 7m*

The national park centre has maps, guides and local information together with displays on the remarkable natural history of the area, local community and work of conservation bodies. Audio-visuals are provided for groups and a 24-hour teletext information service is available.

Times: Open Apr-Oct, daily 10-5; Winter, Sat-Sun, 10-4. Daily in school hols.

Facilities: 🅿 (charged) 🏬 ♿ (Radar key scheme for toilet), toilets for disabled, shop, tours available, audio commentaries available 🚌 (student groups 12 max)

MALTON
Wolds Way Lavender

Deer Farm Park, Sandy Lane, Wintringham, YO17 8HW

☎ 01944 758641

🖹 01944 758641

e-mail: admin@woldswaylavender.co.uk

Web: www.woldswaylavender.co.uk

Dir: *off A64 between Malton & Scarborough, follow brown signs*

The medicinal and therapeutic benefits of lavender are extolled at this 12-acre site close to the Yorkshire Wolds. Four acres are planted with lavender, and there is a wood-burning still for the extraction of lavender oil. Visitors can be calmed by the Sensory Areas and purchase lavender items at the farm shop.

Times: Open daily, wk before 21 Mar-30 Oct, 10-4. May-Aug 10-5

Facilities: 🅿 🍽 (licensed) 🏬 ♿ (sensory garden, raised flower beds), shop, garden centre, tours, audio commentaries ⊗ (ex assist dogs) 🚌 (advise before arrival)

NORTH YORKSHIRE

NORTH YORKSHIRE

REDCAR
RNLI Zetland Museum
5 King Street, TS10 3AH
☎ 01642 485370 & 471813
Dir: *on corner of King St and The Promenade*
The museum portrays the lifeboat, maritime, fishing and local history of the area, including its main exhibit 'The Zetland' - the oldest lifeboat in the world, dating from 1802. There is also a replica of a fisherman's cottage c1900 and almost 2000 other exhibits. The museum is housed in an early lifeboat station, now a listed building.
Times: Open May, Wed 11-4, Sat-Sun 12-4; Jun-Sep Tue-Fri 11-4, Sat-Sun 12-4. Closed Mon.
Facilities: ℗ (20m) (60p per hour) ♿ (ground floor accessible only), shop 🚌

YORK
York Art Gallery
Exhibition Square, YO1 7EW
☎ 01904 687687
🖹 01904 697966
e-mail: www.york.trust.museum
Web: www.york.trust.museum
Dir: *3 min walk from The Minster in city centre*
The gallery is remarkable for the range and quality of its collections that provide a survey of most developments in Western European painting over the past six centuries. Works by Parmigianino, Bellotto, Lely, Reynolds, Frith, Boudin, Lowry and Nash and nudes by Etty are on permanent display. There are also fine collections of watercolours and pottery.
Times: *Open all year, daily 10-5. (Closed 25 & 26 Dec & 1 Jan).
Facilities: ℗ (500yds) ⊡ ⊼ (chair lift) toilets for disabled, shop, tours available ⊗ (ex assist dogs) 🚌 (advance booking required)

YORK
National Railway Museum
Leeman Road, YO26 4XJ

☎ 01904 621261

📄 01904 611112

e-mail: nrm@nmsi.ac.uk

Web: http://www.nrm.org.uk

Dir: *behind rail station. Signed from all major roads and city centre*

This is the world's largest railway museum. See The Flying Scotsman, three enormous galleries, interactive exhibits and daily events. Until Jan 2009, visitors can ride on the London Eye-style Norwich Union Yorkshire Wheel (for a charge).

Times: Open all year, daily 10-6. Closed 24-26 Dec.

Facilities: ❷ (charged) ℗ (100 yds) (coach parking must be pre-booked) 🖵 🍽 (licensed) 🚻 ♿, ("Please Touch" evenings usually in June), toilets for disabled, shop, garden centre ⊗ (ex assist dogs) 🚌 (free parking if pre-booked)

YORK
Guildhall
Coney Street, YO1 9QN

☎ 01904 613161

📄 01904 551052

Web: www.york.gov.uk

Dir: *5-10mins walk from rail station*

The present Hall dates from 1446 but in 1942 an air raid virtually destroyed the building. The present Guildhall was carefully restored as an exact replica and was re-opened in 1960. There is an interesting arch-braced roof decorated with colourful bosses and supported by 12 solid oak pillars. There are also some beautiful stained-glass windows.

Times: *Open all year, May-Oct, Mon-Fri 9-5, Sat 10-5, Sun 2-5; Nov-Apr, Mon-Fri 9-5.

Facilities: ℗ (15-20 mins walk) ♿ (electric chair lift & ramps), toilets for disabled ⊗ (ex assist dogs)

NORTH YORKSHIRE

SOUTH YORKSHIRE

CONISBROUGH
Conisbrough Castle
DN12 3HH
☎ 01709 863329
Web: www.english-heritage.org.uk
Dir: *NE of town centre off A630*

The white, circular keep of this 12th-century castle is a spectacular structure. Made of magnesian limestone, it is the oldest of its kind in England. Now restored, with two new floors and a roof, it is a fine example of medieval architecture and was the inspiration for Sir Walter Scott's classic novel Ivanhoe.

Times: Open all year, Apr-Sep, daily 10-5 (last admission 4.20); Oct-Mar, daily 10-4 (last admission 3.20). Closed over Xmas period. Please call for details

Facilities: ❷ ⊽ ὠ (wheelchair access limited), shop ⊗ 🚍

DONCASTER
Doncaster Museum & Art Gallery
Chequer Rd, DN1 2AE
☎ 01302 734293
🖷 01302 735409
e-mail: museum@doncaster.gov.uk
Web: www.doncaster.gov.uk/museums
Dir: *off inner ring road*

The wide-ranging collections include fine and decorative art and sculpture. Also ceramics, glass, silver, and displays on history, archaeology and natural history. The historical collection of the Kings Own Yorkshire Light Infantry is housed here. A recent addition is the By River and Road gallery, which details the history of the Doncaster area. Temporary exhibitions are held.

Times: Open all year, Mon-Sat 10-5, Sun 2-5. Closed Good Fri, 25-26 Dec & 1 Jan.

Facilities: ❷ Ⓟ (200yds) Pay & display ὠ (lift, hearing loop in lecture room), toilets for disabled, on first floor, shop ⊗ (ex assist dogs) 🚍

SHEFFIELD
Millennium Galleries

Arundel Gate, S1 2PP

☎ 0114 278 2600

▤ 0114 278 2604

e-mail: info@sheffieldgalleries.org.uk

Web: www.sheffieldgalleries.org.uk

With four different galleries under one roof, the Millennium Galleries has something for everyone. Enjoy new blockbuster exhibitions drawn from the collections of Britain's national galleries and museums, including the Victoria & Albert Museum and Tate Gallery. See the best of contemporary craft and design in a range of exhibitions. Be dazzled by Sheffield's magnificent and internationally important collection of decorative and domestic metal-work and silverware. Discover the Ruskin Gallery with its wonderful array of treasures by Victorian artist and writer John Ruskin.

Times: *Open daily Mon-Sat 10-5, Sun 11-5.

Facilities: ℗ ⊑ ⦿ (licensed) & (hearing loop) toilets for disabled, shop ⊗ (ex assist dogs) 🚌

BRADFORD
Bolling Hall

Bowling Hall Road, BD4 7LP

☎ 01274 431826

▤ 01274 726220

Web: www.bradfordmuseums.org

Dir: *1m from city centre off A650*

A classic West Yorkshire manor house, complete with galleried 'housebody' (hall), Bolling Hall dates mainly from the 17th century but has medieval and 18th-century sections. It has panelled rooms, plasterwork in original colours, heraldic glass and a rare Chippendale bed.

Times: Open all year, Wed-Fri 11-4, Sat 10-5, Sun 12-5. Closed Mon ex BH, Good Fri, 25-26 Dec.

Facilities: ℗ ℗ on street & shop ⊗ (ex assist dogs) 🚌

WEST YORKSHIRE

BRADFORD
Cartwright Hall Art Gallery

Lister Park, BD9 4NS

☎ 01274 431212

🖷 01274 481045

e-mail: cartwright.hall@bradford.gov.uk

Web: www.bradfordmuseums.org

Dir: *1m from city centre on A650*

Built in dramatic Baroque style in 1904, the gallery has permanent collections of 19th and 20th-century British art, contemporary prints, and older works by British and European masters.

Times: Open all year, Tue-Sat 10-5, Sun 1-5. Closed Mon ex BH, Good Fri, 25-26 Dec.

Facilities: ❷ ℗ ♿ (wheelchair available, lift, on street parking available for disabled and for functions), toilets for disabled, shop ⊗ (ex assist dogs) 🚌

BRADFORD
Bradford Industrial Museum and Horses at Work

Moorside Mills, Moorside Road, Eccleshill, BD2 3HP

☎ 01274 435900

🖷 01274 636362

Web: www.bradfordmuseums.org

Dir: *off A658*

Moorside Mills is an original spinning mill, now part of a museum that brings vividly to life the story of Bradford's woollen industry. There is the machinery that once converted raw wool into cloth, and the mill yard rings with the sound of iron on stone as shire horses pull trams, haul buses and give rides. Daily demonstrations and changing exhibitions.

Times: Open all year, Tue-Sat 10-5, Sun 12-5. Closed Mon ex BH, Good Fri, 25-26 Dec

Facilities: ℗ ⊡ (licensed) ♿ , (induction loop in lecture theatre, lift), toilets for disabled, shop ⊗ (ex assist dogs) 🚌

GOMERSAL

Red House

Oxford Road, Cleckheaton, BD19 4JP

☎ 01274 335100

🖹 01274 335105

Web: www.kirkleesmc.gov.uk/community/muse
ums.museum.shtml

Dir: *M62 junct 26, take A58 towards Leeds
then right onto A651 towards Gomersal. Red
House on right*

Delightful redbrick house displayed as the
1830s home of a Yorkshire wool clothier and
merchant. The house and family was visited
by Charlotte Bronte in the 1830s and featured
in her novel Shirley. The gardens have been
reconstructed in the style of the period.

Times: *Open all year, Mon-Fri 11-5, Sat-
Sun 12-5. Telephone for Xmas opening.
Closed Good Fri & 1 Jan.

Facilities: 🅿 🅟 (roadside 100 yds) (difficult
between 3-3.30) ⌘ (Braille/T-setting hearing
aid available) toilets for disabled, shop
⊗ (ex assist dogs) 🚌 (booking essential)

HALIFAX

Bankfield Museum

Boothtown Rd, Akroyd Park, HX3 6HG

☎ 01422 354823 & 352334

🖹 01422 349020

e-mail: bankfield-museum@calderdale.gov.uk

Web: www.calderdale.gov.uk

Dir: *on A647 Bradford via Queensbury road,
0.5m from Halifax town centre*

Built by Edward Akroyd in the 1860s, this
Renaissance-style building is set in parkland
overlooking the town. It has an outstanding
collection of costumes and textiles from many
periods and parts of the world, including a
new gallery featuring East European textiles.
Section on toys, and the museum of the Duke
of Wellington's Regiment is housed here.

Times: *Open all year, Tue-Sat 10-5, Sun
1-4, BH Mon 10-5.

Facilities: 🅿 🅟 (50yds) (restricted access
for coaches) ⌘ (audio guide & tactile
objects), toilets for disabled, shop
⊗ (ex assist dogs) 🚌

WEST YORKSHIRE

WEST YORKSHIRE

HALIFAX
Halifax Visitor Centre and Art Gallery

HX1 1RE

☎ 01422 368725

e-mail: halifax@ytbtic.co.uk

Web: www.calderdale.gov.uk

Dir: *follow brown tourist signs, close to railway station*

The merchants of Halifax built the elegant and unique hall in 1770, and it has over 300 merchant's rooms around a courtyard, now housing an art gallery and visitor centre. There are around eight temporary exhibitions each year.

Times: *Open all year daily. Closed 25-26 Dec. Art Gallery, Tue-Sun & BH Mon 10-5.

Facilities: Ⓟ (50 yds) ⬜ ⌷ & (lifts, shop-mobility on site & audio guide available) toilets for disabled, shop
⊗ (ex assist dogs) 🚌

HUDDERSFIELD
Tolson Memorial Museum

Ravensknowle Park, Wakefield Road, HD5 8DJ

☎ 01484 223830

🖷 01484 223843

e-mail: tolson.museum@kirkdees.gov.uk

Web: tolson.museum.co.uk

Dir: *on A629, 1m from town centre*

Displays on the development of the cloth industry and a collection of horse-drawn vehicles, together with natural history, archaeology, toys and folk exhibits. There is a full programme of events and temporary exhibitions.

Times: *Open all year. Mon-Fri 11-5, Sat & Sun noon-5. Closed Xmas.

Facilities: Ⓟ Ⓟ 100m & (mini-com, partial stairlift, induction loop, parking) toilets for disabled, access toilet, large room with alarm, shop ⊗ (ex assist dogs) 🚌

ILKLEY

Manor House Gallery & Museum

Castle Yard, Church Street, LS29 9DT

☎ 01943 600066

🖹 01943 817079

Web: www.bradfordmuseums.org

Dir: *behind Ilkley Parish Church, on A65*

This Elizabethan manor house, one of Ilkley's few buildings to pre-date the 19th century, was built on the site of a Roman fort. Part of the Roman wall can be seen, together with Roman objects and displays on archaeology. There is a collection of 17th and 18th-century farmhouse parlour and kitchen furniture, and the art gallery exhibits works by contemporary artists and craftspeople.

Times: Open all year, Tue-Sat 1-5, Sun 1-4. Open BH Mon. Closed Good Fri, 25-28 Dec.

Facilities: ℗ (5mins) க shop ⊗ (ex assist dogs) 🚌

KEIGHLEY

Cliffe Castle Museum & Gallery

Spring Gardens Lane, BD20 6LH

☎ 01535 618230

🖹 01535 610536

Web: www.bradfordmuseums.org

Dir: *NW of town off A629*

Built as a millionaire's mansion, the house displays Victorian interiors, together with collections of local and natural history, ceramics, dolls, geological items and minerals. There is a play area and aviary in the grounds. Temporary exhibitions throughout the year.

Times: Open all year, Tue-Sat 10-5, Sun 12-5. Open BH Mon. Closed Good Fri & 25-28 Dec.

Facilities: ℗ ⊑ (licensed) 🪑 க toilets for disabled, shop, garden centre ⊗ (ex assist dogs) 🚌

WEST YORKSHIRE

WEST YORKSHIRE

LEEDS
Kirkstall Abbey
Abbey Road, Kirkstall, LS5 3EH

☎ 0113 230 5492

e-mail: abbey.house@leeds.gov.uk

Web: www.leeds.gov.uk

Dir: *off A65, W of city centre*

The most complete 12th-century Cistercian Abbey in the country stands on the banks of the River Aire. Many of the original buildings can still be seen, including the cloister, church and refectory. Regular tours take visitors to areas not normally accessible to the public. During the summer the Abbey hosts plays, fairs and musical events. A new visitor centre gives an insight into the history of the Abbey.

Times: Open all year. Abbey site open dawn to dusk. The visitor centre is open: Summer, Tue-Sun, 11-4. Winter, Tue-Sun, 11-3.

Facilities: ❷ 🪑 ♿ toilets for disabled, shop, tours available 🚌 (min 10 people)

LEEDS
Royal Armouries Museum
Armouries Drive, LS10 1LT

☎ 0113 220 1999 & 0990 106 666

🖹 0113 220 1955

e-mail: enquiries@armouries.org.uk

Web: www.royalarmouries.org

Dir: *off A61 close to Leeds centre, follow brown heritage signs*

The museum is home for the renowned national collection of arms and armour, which is divided between five galleries: War, Tournament, Self-Defence, Hunting and Oriental. The Hall of Steel features a 100ft-high mass of 3000 pieces of arms and armour. Visitors can handle some of the items. Demonstrations throughout the year.

Times: Open daily, 10-5. Closed 24-25 Dec

Facilities: ❷ (charged) 🖵 🍴 (licensed) 🪑 ♿ (induction loops, wheelchairs, signers, low level counter), toilets for disabled (on ground, second & fourth floors), shop ⊗ (ex assist dogs) 🚌

LEEDS
Leeds City Art Gallery

The Headrow, LS1 3AA

☎ 0113 247 8248

🖺 0113 244 9689

e-mail: city.art.gallery@leeds.gov.uk

Web: www.leeds.gov.uk/artgallery

Dir: *in city centre, next to town hall and library*

Home to one of the best collections of 20th-century British art outside London, as well as Victorian and late 19th-century pictures, an outstanding collection of English watercolours, a display of modern sculpture and temporary exhibitions focusing on contemporary art. Active events programme with talks, demonstrations and workshops.

Times: *Open all year, Mon-Sat 10-5, Wed until 8, Sun 1-5. Closed BHs.

Facilities: ℗ (street parking) 🖵 🍽 (licensed) ♿ (restricted access to upper floor, access ramp), toilets for disabled, shop ⊗ (ex assist dogs) 🚌 (pre-booking advised)

WAKEFIELD
Wakefield Art Gallery

Wentworth Terrace, WF1 3QW

☎ 01924 305796

🖺 01924 305770

e-mail: museumsandarts@wakefield.gov.uk

Web: www.wakefield.gov.uk/cultureandleisure

Dir: *N of city centre by Wakefield College and Clayton Hospital*

Wakefield was home to two of Britain's greatest modern sculptors - Barbara Hepworth and Henry Moore. The art gallery, which has an important collection of 20th-century paintings and sculptures, has a special room devoted to these two local artists. There are frequent temporary exhibitions of both modern and earlier works.

Times: Open all year, Tue-Sat 10.30-4.30, Sun 2-4.30.

Facilities: ℗ (on street parking restricted to 2hrs) 🍴 ♿ shop ⊗ (ex assist dogs) 🚌 (pre-book required)

WEST YORKSHIRE

WEST YORKSHIRE/GUERNSEY

WAKEFIELD
National Coal Mining Museum for England

Caphouse Colliery, New Road, Overton, WF4 4RH

☎ 01924 848806

📄 01924 844567

e-mail: info@ncm.org.uk

Web: www.ncm.org.uk

Dir: *on A642 between Huddersfield & Horbury*

A unique opportunity to go 140 metres underground down one of Britain's oldest working mines with one of the museum's experienced local miners. Models and machinery depict methods and conditions of mining from the early 1800s to present day. Strongly advised to wear sensible footwear and warm clothing.

Times: Open all year, daily 10-5. Closed 24-26 Dec & 1 Jan.

Facilities: ℗ ⌨ 🍽 (licensed) 🍴 ♿ , (induction loop, audio tours, 2 w/chairs for underground), toilets for disabled, shop ⊗ (ex assist dogs) 🚌

VALE
Rousse Tower

Rousse Tower Headland

☎ 01481 726518 & 726965

📄 01481 715177

e-mail: p.sarl@museums.gov.gg

Web: www.museum.guernsey.net

Dir: *on Guernsey's W coast, signed*

One of the original fifteen towers built in 1778-9 in prime defensive positions around the coast of Guernsey. They were designed primarily to prevent the landing of troops on nearby beaches. Musket fire could be directed on invading forces through the loopholes. An interpretation centre displays replica guns.

Times: *Open Apr-Oct 9-dusk, Nov-Mar Wed, Sat & Sun 9-4.

Facilities: ℗ (50yds) ⊗ (ex assist dogs) 🚌 (only room for 5 at a time)

LA GREVE DE LECQ

Greve de Lecq Barracks

St Mary

☎ 01534 483193 & 482238

🖹 01534 485873

e-mail: enquiries@nationaltrustjersey.org.je

Web: www.nationaltrustjersey.org.je

Dir: *on side of valley, overlooking beach*

Originally serving as an outpost of the British Empire, these barracks, built in 1810, were used for civilian housing from the end of WWI to 1972, when they were bought by the National Trust and made into a museum that depicts the life of soldiers who were stationed here in the 19th century. Also includes a collection of old horse-drawn carriages.

Times: *Open: 4 Jun-25 Sept, Sun only.

Facilities: Ⓟ (100yds) ♿ (wheelchair ramps), toilets for disabled (located in ground floor toilets), shop 🚫 (ex assist dogs)

ST OUEN

Kempt Tower Visitor Centre

Five Mile Road

☎ 01534 483651 & 483140

🖹 01534 485289

The centre has displays on history and the wildlife of St Ouen's Bay, including Les Mielles, which is Jersey's miniature national park. Nature walks are held every Thursday (May to September). Check local press for details.

Times: *Open BHs, Apr & Oct, Thu & Sun only 2-5; May-Sep, daily (ex Mon) 2-5.

Facilities: Ⓟ ⛩ shop 🚫 🚌

ISLE OF MAN

CASTLETOWN
Old Grammar School
IM9 1LE
☎ 01624 648000
🖹 01624 648001
e-mail: enquiries@mnh.gov.im
Web: www.storyofmann.com
Dir: *centre of Castletown, opposite the castle*
Built around 1200AD, the former capital's first church, St Mary's, has had a significant role in Manx education. It was a school from 1570 to 1930 and evokes memories of Victorian school life.
Times: Open daily, Etr-late Oct, 10-5.
Facilities: ℗ (30 yards) (Disc Zone Parking) ⴲ shop ⊗ (ex assist dogs) 🚌 (pre-booking advised)

DOUGLAS
Manx Museum
IM1 3LY
☎ 01624 648000
🖹 01624 648001
e-mail: enquiries@mnh.gov.im
Web: www.storyofmann.com
Dir: *signed in Douglas*
The Island's treasure house provides an exciting introduction to the 'Story of Mann' where a specially produced film portrayal of Manx history complements the displays. Galleries depict natural history, archaeology and the social development of the Island. There are examples of famous Manx artists in the National Art Gallery together with the Island's National archive and reference library
Times: Open daily all year, Mon-Sat, 10-5. Closed 25-26 Dec & 1 Jan.
Facilities: ℗ (30yds) (parking discs required) ⴱ 🍽 (licensed) ⴲ ⴵ (lift), toilets for disabled, shop, audio commentaries ⊗ (ex assist dogs) 🚌 (pre-booking advised)

PORT ST MARY
Sound Visitor Centre
The Sound, IM1 3LY

☎ 01624 648000 & 838123

🖻 01624 648001

e-mail: enquiries@mnh.gov.im

Web: www.storyofmann.com

Dir: *follow coastal road towards Port Erin/Port St Mary. Past Cregneash village towards most S point of Island*

The Sound Visitor Centre is set in one of the Island's most scenic areas overlooking the natural wonders of the Sound and the Calf of Man. Along with information and audio presentations about the area, a new car park and high quality refreshments are provided for the enjoyment and convenience of visitors.

Times: Open daily, Etr-Oct 10-5. For Winter opening times telephone 01624 838123.

Facilities: ❷ ⌷ ⭐ (licensed) ☵ ♿ toilets for disabled, audio commentaries available 🚍

ABERDEEN
Aberdeen Art Gallery
Schoolhill, AB10 1FQ

☎ 01224 523700

🖻 01224 632133

e-mail: info@aagm.co.uk

Web: http://www.aagm.co.uk

Dir: *located in city centre*

One of the city's most popular tourist attractions Aberdeen's splendid art gallery houses an important fine art collection with many 19th and 20th century works.

Times: *Open all year Mon-Sat 10-5, Sun 2-5. Closed Xmas & New Year

Facilities: ℗ (500yds) ⌷ ♿ (ramp, lift) toilets for disabled, shop ⊗ (ex assist dogs) 🚍

ABERDEEN
Cruickshank Botanic Garden
University of Aberdeen, St Machar Drive,
AB24 3UU
☎ 01224 272704
🖹 01224 272703
e-mail: pss@abdn.ac.uk
Web: http://www.abdn.ac.uk/pss/cruickshank
Dir: *enter by gate in Chanonry, in Old Aberdeen*

Developed at the end of the 19th century, the 11 acres include rock and water gardens, a rose garden, a fine herbaceous border, an arboretum and a patio garden. There are collections of spring bulbs, gentians and alpine plants, and a fine array of trees and shrubs.

Times: *Open all year, Mon-Fri 9-4.30; also Sat & Sun, May-Sep 2-5.
Facilities: ℗ (200yds) ♿ tours available ⊗ 🚌 (by appointment)

ABERDEEN
Aberdeen Maritime Museum
Shiprow, AB11 5BY
☎ 01224 337700
🖹 01224 213066
e-mail: info@aagm.co.uk
Web: www.aagm.co.uk
Dir: *located in city centre*

The museum is in Provost Ross's House, Aberdeen's oldest building (1593). It highlights the city's maritime history, its oil industry, and its shipbuilding.

Times: *Open all year Mon-Sat 10-5, Sun 12-3. Closed Xmas & New Year.
Facilities: ℗ (250yds) ⊑ 🍴 (licensed) ♿ (ramps, lifts), toilets for disabled, shop ⊗ 🚌

ABERDEEN
Provost Skene's House
Guestrow, off Broad St, AB10 1AS
☎ 01224 641086
e-mail: info@aagm.co.uk
Web: www.aagm.co.uk

Experience the epitome of style and elegance in this 16th-century townhouse, furnished and decorated in the styles of earlier times. See changing fashions in the Costume Gallery and view an important cycle of religious paintings in the gallery.

Times: *Open all year Mon-Sat 10-5, Sun 1-4. Closed Xmas & New Year. Telephone for details.

Facilities: Ⓟ (200yds) ⚌ ⊗ (ex assist dogs) 🚌

BANCHORY
Banchory Museum
Bridge Street, AB31 5SX
☎ 01771 622807
🖷 01771 623558
e-mail: heritage@aberdeenshire.gov.uk
Dir: *in Bridge St beside tourist information centre*

The museum has displays on Scott Skinner (The 'Strathspey King'), natural history, royal commemorative china, local silver artefacts and a variety of local history displays.

Times: *Open May, Jun & Sep, Oct, Mon, Fri, Sat 11-1 & 2-4; Jul-Aug, Mon-Wed, Fri-Sat, 11-1, 2-4.

Facilities: Ⓟ (100yds) (limited) ♿ toilets for disabled ⊗ (ex assist dogs) 🚌 (pre-booking preferred)

ABERDEENSHIRE

BANFF
Banff Museum
High Street, AB45 1AE
☎ 01771 622807
🖷 01771 623558
e-mail: heritage@aberdeenshire.gov.uk
Displays of geology, natural history, local history, Banff silver, arms and armour, and displays relating to James Ferguson (18th-century astronomer) and Thomas Edward (19th-century Banff naturalist).
Times: *Open Jun-Sep, Mon-Sat 2-4.30.
Facilities: Ⓟ (200yds) ♿ ground floor only access ⊗ (ex assist dogs) 🚌 (pre-booking preferred)

HUNTLY
Brander Museum
The Square, AB54 8AE
☎ 01771 622807
🖷 01771 623558
e-mail: heritage@aberdeenshire.gov.uk
Dir: *in centre of Huntly, sharing building with library. Museum on ground floor*
The museum has displays of local and church history, plus the 19th-century Anderson Bey and the Sudanese campaigns. Exhibits connected with George MacDonald, author and playwright, can also be seen.
Times: *Open all year, Tue-Sat 2-4.30.
Facilities: Ⓟ (25yds) ♿ (access difficult due to 3 large steps at entrance) ⊗ (ex assist dogs) 🚌 (pre-booking necessary)

INVERURIE
Carnegie Museum

Town House, The Square, AB51 3SN

☎ 01771 622807

🖹 01771 623558

e-mail: heritage@aberdeenshire.gov.uk

Dir: *in centre of Inverurie, on left side of townhouse building, above library*

This fine museum contains displays on local history and archaeology, including Pictish stones, Bronze Age material and the Great North of Scotland Railway.

Times: *Open all year, Mon & Wed-Fri 2-4.30, Sat 10-1 & 2-4. Closed Tue & public hols.

Facilities: Ⓟ (50yds) ⊗ (ex assist dogs) 🚌 (pre-booking preferred)

MINTLAW
Aberdeenshire Farming Museum

Aden Country Park, AB42 5FQ

☎ 01771 622807

🖹 01771 623558

e-mail: heritage@aberdeenshire.gov.uk

Web: www.aberdeenshire.gov.uk/heritage

Dir: *1m W of Mintlaw on A950*

Housed in 19th-century farm buildings, once part of the estate which now makes up the Aden Country Park. Two centuries of farming history is illustrated, and the story of the estate is told. The reconstructed Hareshowe farm shows how a family farmed during the 1950s - access by guided tour only.

Times: *Open May-Sep, daily 11-4.30; Apr & Oct, wknds only noon-4.30. (Last admission 30 mins before closing). Park open all year, Apr-Sep 7-10, winter 7-7.

Facilities: Ⓟ (charged) ⟁ 🍴 ♿ (sensory garden) toilets for disabled tours available ⊗ (ex assist dogs) 🚌 (pre-booking essential)

ABERDEENSHIRE

ABERDEENSHIRE

OLD DEER
Deer Abbey
☎ 01466 793191
Web: www.historic-scotland.gov.uk
Dir: *2m W of Mintlaw on A950*
The remains of the Cistercian Abbey, founded in 1218, include the infirmary, Abbot's House and the southern claustral range. The University Library at Cambridge now houses the famous Book of Deer.
Times: *Open at all reasonable times.
Facilities: ℗ ⊗ ▮

PETERHEAD
Arbuthnot Museum
St Peter Street, AB42 1QD
☎ 01771 622807
🖷 01771 623558
e-mail: heritage@aberdeenshire.gov.uk
Dir: *at St.Peter St & Queen St x-roads, above library*
Specialising in local exhibits, particularly those relating to the fishing industry, this museum also displays Arctic and whaling specimens and a British coin collection. The regular programme of exhibitions changes approximately every six weeks.
Times: *Open all year, Mon, Tue & Thu-Sat 11-1 & 2-4.30, Wed 11-1. Closed Sun and BHs.
Facilities: ℗ (150 yds) ⊗ (ex assist dogs) ▦ (pre-booking preferred)

STONEHAVEN
Tolbooth Museum
Old Pier, AB39 2JU

☎ 01771 622807

🖹 01771 623558

e-mail: heritage@aberdeenshire.gov.uk
Dir: *on harbour front*

Built in the late 16th century as a storehouse for the Earls Marischal at Dunnottar Castle, the building was the Kincardineshire County Tollbooth from 1600-1767. Displays feature local history and fishing.

Times: *Open May-16 Oct, Wed-Mon, 1.30-4.30. Closed Tue.

Facilities: ℗ (20yds) ♿ ⊗ (ex assist dogs) 🚌 (pre-booking preferred)

ARBROATH
Arbroath Museum
Signal Tower, Ladyloan, DD11 1PU

☎ 01241 875598

🖹 01241 439263

e-mail: signal.tower@angus.gov.uk
Web: www.angus.gov.uk/history/museums
Dir: *on A92 adjacent to harbour. 16m NE of Dundee*

Fish and Arbroath Smokies, textiles and engineering feature at this local history museum housed in the 1813 shore station of Stevenson's Bell Rock lighthouse. 2007 is the 200th anniversary of the commencement of building of Bell Rock lighthouse.

Times: *Open all year, Mon-Sat 10-5; Jul-Aug, Sun 2-5. Closed 25-26 Dec & 1-2 Jan.

Facilities: ℗ (100yds) 🍴 ♿ (induction loop) shop, tours available ⊗ (ex assist dogs) 🚌 (pre-booking required)

ABERDEENSHIRE/ANGUS

ANGUS

BRECHIN

Brechin Town House Museum

28 High Street, DD9 7AA

☎ 01356 625536

e-mail: brechin.museum@angus.gov.uk

Web: www.angus.gov.uk/history/museum

Dir: *off A90 at sign for Brechin, 2m into town centre*

Within a former courtroom, debtor's prison and seat of local government, this museum covers the history of the little City of Brechin from the earliest settlement, through the market town to the industrialisation in the form of flax, jute mills, distilling, weaving and engineering. Brechin's fascinating history of development is portrayed in vivid displays.

Times: *Open Mon-Tue & Thu-Sat 10-5, Wed 10-1

Facilities: ℗ (150yds) (2hrs max in free car park) ♿ toilets for disabled, purpose built toilet, shop, tours available ⊗ (ex assist dogs) 🚌 (must pre-book)

FORFAR

The Meffan Art Gallery & Museum

20 West High Street, DD8 1BB

☎ 01307 464123 & 467017

🖹 01307 468451

e-mail: the.meffan@angus.gov.uk

Web: www.angus.gov/history/museum

Dir: *off A90, 13m N of Dundee. Attraction in town centre*

This lively, ever-changing contemporary art gallery and museum are full of surprises. Walk down a cobbled street full of shops, ending up at a witch-burning scene! Carved Pictish stones and a diorama of an archaeological dig complete the vibrant displays.

Times: Open all year. Closed 25-26 Dec & 1-2 Jan.

Facilities: ℗ (150yds) (30 mins limit on street) ♿ (handrails, wide door, portable ramp), toilets for disabled, shop, tours available ⊗ (ex assist dogs) 🚌 (pre-booking required)

KIRRIEMUIR

Kirriemuir Gateway to Glens Museum

The Town House, 32 High Street, DD8 4BB

☎ 01575 575479

e-mail: kirrie.gateway@angus.gov.uk

Web: www.angus.gov.uk/history/museum

Dir: *in town centre square*

Housed in the town house dating from 1604, this museum covers the history of Kirriemuir and the Angus Glens from prehistoric times. A realistic model of Kirriemuir on market day in 1604 can be seen and local voices can be heard telling their part in the area's history from sweet making to linen weaving. Animals and birds can be seen at close range in the Wildlife diorama.

Times: Open Mon-Wed, Fri & Sat 10-5, Thu 2-5

Facilities: ℗ (200yds) (free car park) ♿ toilets for disabled, purpose built toilet, shop, tours available ⊗ (ex assist dogs) 🚌 (must pre-book)

MONTROSE

Montrose Museum & Art Gallery

Panmure Place, DD10 8HE

☎ 01674 673232

e-mail: montrose.museum@angus.gov.uk

Web: www.angus.gov.uk/history/museum

Dir: *opposite Montrose Academy in town centre, approach via A92 from Aberdeen or Dundee*

Extensive local collections cover the history of Montrose from prehistoric times, the maritime history of the port, the natural history of Angus, and local art.

Times: Open all year, Mon-Sat 10-5. Closed 25-26 Dec & 1-2 Jan.

Facilities: ℗ (20yds) ♿ shop, tours available ⊗ (ex assist dogs) 🚌 (pre-booking required)

ANGUS

ARGYLL & BUTE

ARROCHAR
Argyll Forest Park

Forestry Commission, Ardgartan Visitor
Centre, G83 7AR

☎ 01301 702597

🖻 01301 702597

e-mail: robin.kennedy@forestry.gsl.gov.uk

Dir: *on A83 at foot of "The Rest and Be
Thankful"*

This park extends over a large area of hill
ground and forest, noted for its rugged
beauty. Numerous forest walks and picnic
sites allow exploration; the Arboretum walks
and the route between Younger Botanic
Gardens and Puck's Glen are particularly
lovely.

Times: Open all year.

Facilities: ❷ (no overnight parking)
🏳 shop 🚐

CARNASSERIE CASTLE
Carnasserie Castle

Lochgilphead, PA31 8RQ

Web: www.historic-scotland.gov.uk

Dir: *2m N of Kilmartin off A816*

A handsome combined tower house and hall,
home of John Carswell, first Protestant
Bishop of the Isles and translator of the first
book printed in Gaelic. Very fine architectural
details of the late 16th century.

Times: *Open at all reasonable times.

Facilities: ⊗ 🋘

KILMARTIN
Dunadd Fort

Web: www.historic-scotland.gov.uk

Dir: *2m S of Kilmartin on A816*

Dunadd was one of the ancient capitals of Dalriada from which the Celtic kingdom of Scotland was formed. Near to this prehistoric hill fort (now little more than an isolated hillock) are carvings of a boar and a footprint; these probably marked the spot where early kings were invested with their royal power.

Times: *Open at all reasonable times.

Facilities: ⊗ 🚩

ROTHESAY
Ardencraig

PA20 9HA

☎ 01700 504225

🖷 01700 504225

e-mail: allan.macdonald@argyll-bute.co.uk

Web: www.argyll-bute.gov.uk

Dir: *1m off A844, S of Rothesay*

Particular attention has been paid to improving the layout of the garden and introducing rare plants. The greenhouse and walled garden produce plants for floral displays throughout the district. A variety of fish are kept in the ornamental ponds and the aviaries have some interesting birds.

Times: *Open May-Sep.

Facilities: ℗ (200yds) (coach access difficult) ⛱ ♿ ⊗ (ex assist dogs) 🚌 (by arrangement)

ARGYLL & BUTE

NORTH AYRSHIRE

IRVINE
Vennel Gallery

10 Glasgow Vennel, KA12 0BD

☎ 01294 275059

🖶 01294 275059

e-mail: vennel@north-ayrshire.gov.uk

Web: www.north-ayrshire.gov.uk/museums

The Vennel Gallery has a reputation for exciting and varied exhibitions, ranging from international to local artists. Behind the museum is the Heckling Shop where Robert Burns, Scotland's most famous poet, spent part of his youth learning the trade of flax dressing.There is an audio-visual programme on Burns, as well as a reconstruction of his lodgings at No.4 Glasgow Vennel, Irvine.

Times: *Open all year, Thu-Sun 10-1 & 2-5

Facilities: ℗ (residential area) ♿ toilets for disabled, shop, tours available ⊗ (ex assist dogs) 🚍

MILLPORT
Museum of the Cumbraes

Garrison Grounds, KA28 0DG

☎ 01475 531191

e-mail: namuseum@north-ayrshire.gov.uk

Web: www.north-ayrshire.gov.uk/museums

Dir: *Ferry to Millport, from Largs Cal-Mac Terminal. Bus meets each ferry*

A small museum which displays the history and life of the Cumbraes. There is also a fine collection of local photographs.

Times: *Open Etr-Sep, Thu-Mon 10-1 & 2-5.

Facilities: ℗ (50yds, on street) ♿ shop, tours available ⊗ (ex assist dogs) 🚍 (pre-booking preferred)

SALTCOATS

North Ayrshire Museum

Manse Street, Kirkgate, KA21 5AA

☎ 01294 464174

🖹 01294 464174

e-mail: namuseum@north-ayrshire.gov.uk

Web: www.north-ayrshire.gov.uk/museums

Dir: *town centre*

This museum is housed in an 18th-century church, and features a rich variety of artefacts from the North Ayrshire area, including archaeological and social history material. There is a continuing programme of temporary exhibitions.

Times: *Open all year, Mon-Sat (ex Sun & Wed) 10-1 & 2-5.

Facilities: ℗ (100yds) ♿ toilets for disabled, shop, tours available ⊗ (ex assist dogs) 🚌 (advance booking, max 40)

ALVA

Mill Trail Visitor Centre

Glentana Mill, West Stirling St, FK12 5EN

☎ 01259 769696

🖹 01259 763100

Dir: *on A91 approx 8m E of Stirling*

In the heart of Scotland's woollen mill country, the Centre recounts the history of Scotland's woollen and tweed traditions, and features machines from spinning wheels to large motorised looms of the type in use today. Hear 12-year-old Mary describe her working day as a mill girl 150 years ago, and then contrast her story with our modern working woollen mill. Factory bargains and local crafts, tourist information centre, café.

Times: *Open all year, Jan-Jun 10-5; Jul-Aug 9-5; Sep-Dec 10-5.

Facilities: ℗ ⊐ 🪑 ♿ toilets for disabled, shop ⊗ (ex assist dogs) 🚌 (pre-booked)

DUMFRIES & GALLOWAY

DRUMCOLTRAN TOWER
Drumcoltran Tower

Web: www.historic-scotland.gov.uk

Dir: *7m NE of Dalbeattie, in farm buildings off A711*

A well-preserved tower of mid 16th-century date simply planned and built, sitting within a busy modern farmyard.

Times: *Open at any reasonable time.

Facilities: ℗ ⊗ ☒

DUMFRIES
Burns Mausoleum

St Michael's Churchyard

☎ 01387 255297

🖷 01387 265081

e-mail: dumfriesmuseum@dumgal.gov.uk

Web: www.dumgal.gov.uk/museums

Dir: *at junct of Brooms Rd (ATS) and St Michael's St (B725)*

The mausoleum is in the form of a Greek temple, and contains the tombs of Robert Burns, his wife Jean Armour, and their five sons. A sculptured group shows the Muse of Poetry flinging her cloak over Burns at the plough.

Times: *Unrestricted access to exterior. Guided tours, and access to interior available from Robert Burns House. Please phone 01387 255297 for details.

Facilities: ℗ (50yds) ♿ (visitors with mobility difficulties tel 01387 255297) 🚌

DUMFRIES
Robert Burns Centre

Mill Road, DG2 7BE

☎ 01387 264808

🗎 01387 265081

e-mail: dumfriesmuseum@dumgal.gov.uk

Web: www.dumgal.gov.uk/museums

Dir: *on Westbank of River Nith*

This award-winning centre explores the connections between Robert Burns and the town of Dumfries. Situated in the town's 18th-century watermill, the centre tells the story of Burns' last years spent in the busy streets and lively atmosphere of Dumfries in the 1790s. In the evening the centre shows feature films in the Film Theatre.

Times: *Open all year, Apr-Sep, daily 10-8 (Sun 2-5); Oct-Mar, Tue-Sat 10-1 & 2-5.

Facilities: ℗ (50yds) (parking disc required-ask at museum) 🖵 🍽 🍴 ♿ (induction loop hearing system in auditorium, chairlift), toilets for disabled, shop 🚌

KIRKCUDBRIGHT
Stewartry Museum

St Mary Street, DG6 4AQ

☎ 01557 331643

🗎 01557 331643

e-mail: david@dumgal.gov.uk

Web: www.dumgal.go.uk/museums

Dir: *from A711 through town, pass parish church, museum approx 200yds on right*

This museum has a large and varied collection of archaeological, social history and natural history exhibits relating to the Stewartry district.

Times: *Open May, Jun & Sep, Mon-Sat 11-5 Sun 2-5; Jul-Aug, Mon-Sat 10-5 Sun 2-5; Oct Mon-Sat 11-4 Sun 2-5; Nov-Apr Mon-Sat 11-4

Facilities: ℗ 🍴 ♿ shop ⊗ (ex assist dogs) 🚌

DUMFRIES & GALLOWAY

KIRKCUDBRIGHT

Tolbooth Art Centre

High Street, DG6 4JL

☎ 01557 331556

🖷 01557 331643

e-mail: davidd@dumgal.gov.uk

Web: www.dumgal.gov.uk/museums

Dir: *from A711, through town pass church & Stewartry Museum, 1st right into High St*

Dating from 1629, the Tolbooth was converted into an art centre and provides an introduction to the Kirkcudbright artists' colony, which flourished from the 1880s. Provides studio and exhibition space for local and visiting artists. Exhibitions from March to October.

Times: *Open May, Jun & Sep, Mon-Sat 11-5 Sun 2-5; Jul & Aug, Mon-Sat 10-5, Sun 2-5; Oct, Mon-Sat 11-4 Sun 2-5; Nov-Apr, Mon-Sat 11-4

Facilities: Ⓟ (on street) ☕ ♿ all parts accessible (lift for access to upper floors) toilets for disabled (hand rails, situated on ground floor), shop, tours available 🚫 (ex assist dogs) 🚌 30 max

NEW ABBEY

Shambellie House Museum of Costume

DG2 8HQ

☎ 01387 850375

🖷 01387 850461

e-mail: info@nms.ac.uk

Web: www.nms.ac.uk/costume

Dir: *7m S of Dumfries, on A710*

Shambellie House is a beautiful Victorian country house set in attractive wooded grounds. You are invited to step back in time and experience Victorian and Edwardian grace and refinement. See period costume from the 1850s to the 1950s displayed in appropriate room settings with accessories, furniture and decorative art. Telephone for details of special events.

Times: Open Apr-Oct, daily, 10-5.

Facilities: Ⓟ ☕ 🪑 ♿ (ramp and w/chair lift at main entrance), shop 🚫 (ex assist dogs) 🚌

PALNACKIE
Orchardton Tower

Web: www.historic-scotland.gov.uk

Dir: *6m SE of Castle Douglas on A711*

A charming little tower house of mid-15th-century date. It is, uniquely, circular in plan.

Times: *Open all reasonable times. Closed 25-26 Dec.

Facilities: ❷ ⊗ ▤

RUTHWELL
Savings Banks Museum

DG1 4NN

☎ 01387 870640

e-mail: tsbmuseum@btinternet.com

Web: www.lloydstsb.com/savingsbankmuseum

Dir: *off B724, 10m E of Dumfries & 7m W of Annan*

Housed in the building where Savings Banks first began, the museum traces their growth and development from 1810 up to the present day. The museum also traces the life of Dr Henry Duncan, father of savings banks, and restorer of the Ruthwell Cross. Multi-lingual leaflets available.

Times: Open, Tue-Sat, Apr-Sep, Thu-Sat, Oct-Mar, 10-4; Open on BHs except Xmas Day & New Year

Facilities: ❷ (adjacent) ♿ (touch facilities for blind, guide available) tours available ⊗ (ex assist dogs) 🚌 (advanced notification required)

DUMFRIES & GALLOWAY

DUMFRIES & GALLOWAY

RUTHWELL
Ruthwell Cross

Web: www.historic-scotland.gov.uk
Dir: *sited within the parish church on B724*

Now in a specially built apse in the parish church, the carved cross dates from the 7th or 8th centuries. Two faces show scenes from the Life of Christ; the others show scroll work, and parts of an ancient poem in Runic characters. It was broken up in the 18th century, but pieced together by a 19th-century minister.

Times: *Open all reasonable times. Contact Key Keeper for access on 01387 870249.
Facilities: ℗ ⊗ 🁉

SANQUHAR
Sanquhar Tolbooth Museum
High Street, DG4 6BN
☎ 01659 250186
🖷 01387 265081
e-mail: dumfriesmuseum@dumgal.gov.uk
Web: www.dumgal.gov.uk/museums
Dir: *on A76 Dumfries-Kilmarnock road*

Housed in the town's fine 18th-century tolbooth, the museum tells the story of the mines and miners of the area, its earliest inhabitants, native and Roman, the history and customs of the Royal Burgh of Sanquhar and local traditions.

Times: *Open Apr-Sep, Tue-Sat 10-1 & 2-5, Sun 2-5.
Facilities: ℗ (50yds) ♿ (museum up steps, phone for info), shop, tours available 🚌

DUNDEE

Broughty Castle Museum

Castle Approach, Broughty Ferry, DD5 2TF

☎ 01382 436916

🖶 01382 436951

e-mail: broughty@dundeecity.gov.uk

Web: www.dundeecity.gov.uk/broughtycastle

Dir: *turn S off A930 at traffic lights by Eastern Primary School in Broughty Ferry*

The 15th-century castle was rebuilt to defend the Tay estuary in the 19th century. It now houses fascinating displays on Dundee's whaling history, arms and armour, local history and seashore life. There are superb views across the Tay estuary from the observation room.

Times: Open all year Apr-Sep, Mon-Sat 10-4, Sun 12.30-4; Oct-Mar, Tue-Sat 10-4, Sun 12.30-4. Closed Mons, 25-26 Dec & 1-3 Jan.

Facilities: ⓟ (50yds) ⌑ (unsuitable for wheelchairs) shop ⊗ (ex assist dogs) ⛟ (pre-booking preferred)

BEARSDEN

Antonine Wall:
Bearsden Bath-house

Roman Road, G61 2SG

Web: www.historic-scotland.gov.uk

Dir: *signed from Bearsden Cross on A810*

Considered to be the best surviving visible Roman building in Scotland, the bath-house was discovered in 1973 during excavations for a construction site. It was originally built for use by the Roman garrison at Bearsden Fort, which is part of the Antonine Wall defences. This building dates from the 2nd century AD. Visitors should wear sensible footwear.

Times: *Open all reasonable times.

Facilities: ♿ ⊗ ⛟

CITY OF DUNDEE/EAST DUNBARTONSHIRE

EAST DUNBARTONSHIRE/CITY OF EDINBURGH

MILNGAVIE
Mugdock Country Park

Craigallian Rd, G62 8EL

☎ 0141 956 6100 & 6586

e-mail: rangers@mcp.ndo.co.uk

Web: www.mugdock-country-park.org.uk

Dir: *N of Glasgow on A81, signed*

This country park incorporates the remains of Mugdock and Craigend castles, set in beautiful landscapes as well as an exhibition centre, craft shops, orienteering course and many walks.

Times: Open all year, daily.

Facilities: ❷ (summer 9-9, winter 9-6) ☟ ⦿ (licensed) ⊞ ⅙ (mobility equipment, audio leaflet, large print media) toilets for disabled, shop, garden centre, tours available, audio commentaries available ⛟ (pre-booked preferred)

EDINBURGH
Museum of Edinburgh

142 Canongate, Royal Mile, EH8 8DD

☎ 0131 529 4143

🖹 0131 557 3346

e-mail: cac.marketing@edinburgh.gov.uk

Web: www.cac.org.uk

Dir: *on the Royal Mile*

Housed in one of the best-preserved 16th-century buildings in the Old Town. It was built in 1570 and later became the headquarters of the Incorporation of Hammermen. Now a museum of local history, it has collections of silver, glassware, pottery, and other items such as street signs.

Times: *Open all year, Mon-Sat 10-5. Sun in Aug noon-5.

Facilities: ℗ (200yds) (parking meters, limited spaces) ⅙ shop ⊗ (ex assist dogs) ⛟ (pre-booking required)

EDINBURGH
The Writers' Museum and Makars' Court

Lady Stair's House, Lady Stair's Close, Lawnmarket, EH1 2PA

☎ 0131 529 4901

🖹 0131 220 5057

e-mail: enquiries@writersmuseum.demon.co.uk

Web: www.cac.org.uk

Dir: *off the Royal Mile*

Situated in the historic Lady Stair's House which dates from 1622, the museum houses various objects associated with Robert Burns, Sir Walter Scott and Robert Louis Stevenson. Temporary exhibitions are planned throughout the year.

Times: *Open all year, Mon-Sat 10-5. (Aug only, Sun 12-5).

Facilities: Ⓟ (500yds) (parking meters) shop ⊗ (ex assist dogs) 🚌 (pre-booking required)

EDINBURGH
Parliament House

Supreme Courts, 2-11 Parliament Square, EH1 1RQ

☎ 0131 225 2595

🖹 0131 240 6755

e-mail: emackenzie@scotcourts.gov.uk

Web: www.scotcourts.gov.uk

Dir: *behind St Giles Cathedral on the high street*

Scotland's independent parliament last sat in 1707, in this 17th-century building hidden behind an 1829 façade, now the seat of the Supreme Law Courts of Scotland. A large stained glass window depicts the inauguration of the Court of Session in 1540.

Times: Open all year, Mon-Fri 10-4.

Facilities: Ⓟ (400yds) (metered parking in high street) 🖵 🍽 �& (stair lift to restaurant), toilets for disabled, tours available ⊗ (ex assist dogs) 🚌

CITY OF EDINBURGH

EDINBURGH
Royal Botanic Garden Edinburgh

Inverleith Row, EH3 5LR

☎ 0131 552 7171

📄 0131 248 2901

e-mail: info@rbge.org.uk

Web: www.rbge.org.uk

Dir: *1m N of city centre, off A902*

Established in 1670, the Garden is now over 70 acres of landscaped grounds. Spectacular features include the Rock Garden and the Chinese Hillside. The amazing glasshouses feature Britain's tallest palm house and the magnificent woodland gardens and arboretum.

Times: *Open all year, daily; Apr-Sep, 10-7; Mar & Oct, 10-6; Nov-Feb, 10-4. Closed 25 Dec & 1 Jan. (Facilities close 30 mins before Garden)

Facilities: ℗ (free on street) (restricted at certain times) ⏇ ⑩ (licensed) ♿ (wheel-chairs at east/west gates), toilets for disabled, shop, garden centre, tours available, audio commentaries ⊗ (ex assist dogs) 🚌

EDINBURGH
Scottish National Gallery of Modern Art

Belford Rd, EH4 3DR

☎ 0131 624 6200

📄 0131 343 3250

e-mail: enquiries@nationalgalleries.org

Web: www.nationalgalleries.org

Dir: *in West End, 20 min walk from Haymarket station*

An outstanding collection of 20th-century painting, sculpture and graphic art. Includes major works by Matisse, Picasso, Bacon, Moore and Lichtenstein and an exceptional group of Scottish paintings. Set in leafy grounds with a sculpture garden.

Times: *Open all year, daily 10-5. 1 Jan noon-5. Closed 25-26 Dec.

Facilities: ❷ ⏇ (licensed) ♿ (ramps & lift), toilets for disabled, shop, tours available ⊗ (ex assist dogs) 🚌

EDINBURGH
Scottish National Portrait Gallery

1 Queen Street, EH2 1JD

☎ 0131 624 6200

▤ 0131 558 3691

e-mail: enquiries@nationalgalleries.org

Web: www.nationalgalleries.org

Dir: *parallel to Princes St, just behind St Andrew Square*

The collection provides a visual history of Scotland from the 16th century to the present day, told through the portraits of the people who shaped it. Among the most famous are Mary, Queen of Scots, Ramsay's portrait of David Hume and Raeburn's portrait of Sir Walter Scott. The building also houses the National Collection of Photography.

Times: *Open all year, daily, 10-5, Thu until 7. 1 Jan noon-5. Closed 25-26 Dec.

Facilities: ℗ (200yds) (pay and display) ⌨ & (ramps & lift) toilets for disabled, shop, tours available ⊗ (ex assist dogs) 🚌 (prior booking preferred)

EDINBURGH
Museum of Childhood

42 High Street, Royal Mile,, EH1 1TG

☎ 0131 529 4142

▤ 0131 558 3103

e-mail: admin@museumofchildhood.fsnet.co.uk

Web: www.cac.org.uk

Dir: *On the Royal Mile*

One of the first museums of its kind, this was the brainchild of a local councillor, and first opened in 1955. It has a wonderful collection of toys, games and other belongings of children through the ages, to delight visitors both old and young. Ring for details of special events.

Times: Open all year, Mon-Sat 10-5, Sun 12-5.

Facilities: ℗ & (3 floors only) toilets for disabled, shop ⊗ (ex assist dogs) 🚌 (advance notice preferred)

CITY OF EDINBURGH

CITY OF EDINBURGH

EDINBURGH
Royal Museum
Chambers St, EH1 1JF
☎ 0131 247 4422
▤ 0131 220 4819
e-mail: info@nms.ac.uk
Web: www.nms.ac.uk
Dir: *in Chambers St, in Old Town, a few mins walk from Princes St and the Royal Mile*

This magnificent museum houses extensive international collections covering the Decorative Arts, Natural History, Science, Technology and Working Life, and Geology. Temporary exhibitions, films, lectures and concerts take place throughout the year.

Times: *Open all year, Mon-Sun 10-5. Closed 25 Dec. Phone for times on 26 Dec/1 Jan.

Facilities: ℗ (on street, metered) ☐ ⑩ (licensed) ♿ (induction loops) toilets for disabled, shop, tours available, audio commentaries available ⊗ (ex assist dogs) 🚌

EDINBURGH
The People's Story
Canongate Tolbooth, 163 Canongate, Royal Mile, EH8 8BN
☎ 0131 529 4057
▤ 0131 556 3439
e-mail: cac.marketing@edinburgh.gov.uk
Web: www.cac.org.uk
Dir: *on the Royal Mile*

The museum, housed in the 16th-century tolbooth, tells the story of the ordinary people of Edinburgh from the late 18th century to the present day. Reconstructions include a prison cell, 1930s pub and 1940s kitchen supported by photographs, displays, sounds and smells.

Times: *Open all year, Mon-Sat 10-5. Also open Sun in Aug 12-5.

Facilities: ℗ (100yds) (parking meters) ♿ (lift, induction loop in video room, touch facilities), toilets for disabled, shop ⊗ (ex assist dogs) 🚌

EDINBURGH
Museum of Scotland

Chambers Street, EH1 1JF

☎ 0131 247 4422

🖹 0131 220 4819

e-mail: info@nms.ac.uk

Web: www.nms.ac.uk

Dir: *in Old Town. A few mins walk from Princes St and The Royal Mile*

Striking landmark in Edinburgh's historic Old Town, housing more than 10,000 of the nation's most precious artefacts, as well as everyday objects which throw light on life in Scotland through the ages. Admission to the adjacent Royal Museum is also free. Telephone for details of special events.

Times: *Open all year, Mon-Sun 10-5. Closed 25 Dec. Please telephone for times on 26 Dec and 1 Jan.

Facilities: ℗ (off street) (metered parking) ⛉ 🍽 (licensed) ♿ toilets for disabled, shop, tours available, audio commentaries ⊗ (ex assist dogs) 🚌

SOUTH QUEENSFERRY
Queensferry Museum

53 High Street, EH30 9HP

☎ 0131 331 5545

🖹 0131 557 3346

Web: www.cac.org.uk

Dir: *A90 from Edinburgh*

The museum commands magnificent views of the two great bridges spanning the Forth and traces the history of the people of Queensferry and Dalmeny, the historic passage to Fife, the construction of the rail and road bridges and the wildlife of the Forth estuary. An ancient annual custom, in August, is Burry Man, who is clad from head to toe in burrs, and parades through the town. See the full size model of the Burry Man in the museum.

Times: Open all year, Mon & Thu-Sat 10-1, 2.15-5, Sun noon-5. (Last admission 1/2 hour before closing). Closed 25-26 Dec & 1-2 Jan

Facilities: ℗ (0.25m) (induction loop at reception) shop ⊗ (ex assist dogs) 🚌 (up to 40 people)

FALKIRK

BO'NESS

Kinneil Museum & Roman Fortlet

Duchess Anne Cottages, Kinniel Estate,
EH51 0PR

☎ 01506 778530

Web: www.falkirk.gov.uk/cultural

Dir: *follow tourist signs from Heritage
Railway, off M9. Establishment at E end of
town accessed via Dean Rd*

The museum is in a converted stable block of
Kinneil House. The ground floor has displays
on the industrial history of Bo'ness, while
the upper floor looks at the history and
environment of the Kinneil Estate. The
remains of the Roman fortlet can be seen
nearby. An audio visual presentation shows
2000 years of history.

Times: Open all year, Mon-Sat 12.30-4.

Facilities: ❷ limited spaces ♿ shop
♻ (ex assist dogs) 🚌 (max 40)

FALKIRK

Callendar House

Callendar Park, FK1 1YR

☎ 01324 503770

🖨 01324 503771

e-mail: callendar.house@falkirk.gov.uk

Web: www.falkirk.gov.uk/cultural

Dir: *S side of town centre, Callendar House
is signposted. Easily accessible from M9*

Mary, Queen of Scots, Oliver Cromwell,
Bonnie Prince Charlie, noble earls and
wealthy merchants all feature in the history
of Callendar House. Costumed interpreters
describe early 19th-century life in the
kitchens and the 900-year history of the
house is illustrated in the 'Story of Callendar
House' exhibition. Regular exhibitions.

Times: Open all year, Mon-Sat ,10-5. Apr-
Sep, Sun, 2-5.

Facilities: ❷ (2 min walk, parking limited to
disabled) ⊡🛋♿ (lifts) toilets for disabled,
shop ♻ (ex assist dogs) 🚌 (pre-booking
required)

FALKIRK
Rough Castle

Web: www.historic-scotland.gov.uk

Dir: *1m E of Bonnybridge, signed from B816*

The impressive earthworks of a large Roman fort on the Antonine Wall can be seen here. The buildings have disappeared, but the mounds and terraces are the sites of barracks, and granary and bath buildings. Running between them is the military road, which once linked all the forts on the wall and is still well defined.

Times: *Open any reasonable time.

Facilities: ℗ ⊗ ♖

BURNTISLAND
Burntisland Edwardian Fair Museum

102 High Street, KY3 9AS

☎ 01592 412860

🖹 01592 412870

Web: kirkcaldy.museum@fife.gov.uk

Dir: *in the centre of Burntisland*

Burntisland Museum has recreated a walk through the sights and sounds of the town's fair in 1910, based on a painting of the scene by local artist Andrew Young. See reconstructed rides, stalls and side shows of the time.

Times: *Open all year, Mon, Wed, Fri & Sat 10-1 & 2-5; Tue & Thu 10-1 & 2-7. Closed PHs)

Facilities: ℗ (20mtrs) (on street parking) ⊗ (ex assist dogs) 🚌 (phone in advance)

FALKIRK/FIFE

FIFE

DUNFERMLINE

Pittencrieff House Museum

Pittencrieff Park, KY12 8QH

☎ 01383 722935 & 313838

🖹 01383 313837

e-mail: dunfermline.museum@fife.gov.uk

Dir: *off A994 into Pittencrieff Park car park.*
Attraction on W edge of town

A fine 17th-century house standing in the
beautiful park gifted to the town by Andrew
Carnegie. Accessible displays tell the story
of the park's animals and plants, with plenty
of photographs of people enjoying the park
over the last 100 years.

Times: *Open all year daily Jan-Mar 11-4;
Apr-Sep 11-5; Oct-Dec 11-4

Facilities: ℗ (800yds) ♿ (ramp) toilets for
disabled, shop ⊗ (ex assist dogs) 🚌

KIRKCALDY

Kirkcaldy Museum & Art Gallery

War Memorial Gardens, KY1 1YG

☎ 01592 412860

🖹 01592 412870

e-mail: kirkcaldy.museum@fife.gov.uk

Web: www.fifedirect.org.uk/museums

Dir: *next to train station*

Set in the town's lovely memorial gardens,
the museum houses a collection of fine and
decorative art, including 18th to 21st-century
Scottish paintings, among them the works
of William McTaggart and S J Peploe. An
award-winning display 'Changing Places' tells
the story of the social, industrial and natural
heritage of the area.

Times: *Open all year, Mon-Sat 10.30-5,
Sun 2-5. Closed local hols

Facilities: ℗ (station car park) ♿ (ramp
to main entrance & lift to 1st floor galleries)
toilets for disabled, shop ⊗ (ex assist dogs)
🚌 (contact museum in advance)

GLASGOW
Glasgow Botanic Gardens

730 Great Western Road, G12 0UE

☎ 0141 334 2422

🖹 0141 339 6964

e-mail: gbg@land.glasgow.gov.uk

Dir: *From M8 junct 17 onto A82 Dumbarton. Approx 2-3m, Botanic Gardens on right*

Home of the national collections of Dendrobium Orchids, Begonias and tree ferns. The Gardens consist of an arboretum, herbaceous borders, a herb garden, rose garden, and unusual vegetables. The Kibble Palace contains carnivorous plants, island flora and temperate plant collections.

Times: *Open all year. Gardens open daily 7-dusk, Glasshouses 10-4.45 (4.15 in winter).

Facilities: ℗ (street parking) ♿ toilets for disabled, key from toilet block attendant, tours available ⊗ 🚍

GLASGOW
Hunterian Museum

Gilbert Scott Building, The University of Glasgow, G12 8QQ

☎ 0141 330 4221

🖹 0141 330 3617

e-mail: hunter@museum.gla.ac.uk

Web: www.hunterian.gla.ac.uk

Dir: *on University of Glasgow campus in Hillhead District, 2m W of city centre*

Named after the 18th-century physician, Dr William Hunter, who bequeathed his large collections of coins, medals, fossils, geological specimens and archaeological and ethnographic items to the university. The exhibits are shown in the main building of the university, and temporary exhibitions are held.

Times: *Open all year, Mon-Sat 9.30-5. Closed certain BHs phone for details.

Facilities: ℗ (100yds) (pay & display) ♿ (lift), toilets for disabled, shop ⊗ (ex assist dogs) 🚍

CITY OF GLASGOW

GLASGOW

Provand's Lordship

3 Castle Street, G4 0RB

☎ 0141 552 8819

🖷 0141 552 4744

e-mail: museums@cls.glsgow.gov.uk

Web: www.glasgowmuseums.com

Dir: *1m E of city centre*

Provand's Lordship is the only house to survive from medieval Glasgow. For over 500 years it has watched the changing fortunes of the city and nearby cathedral. Bishop Andrew Muirhead built the house as part of St Nicholas' Hospital in 1971. The prebendary of Barlanark later bought it for use as a manse. Inside, the displays recreate home life in the middle ages. Behind is St Nicholas Garden, built in 1997, a medical herb garden, in keeping with the original purpose of house.

Times: *Open all year, Mon-Thu & Sat 10-5, Fri & Sun 11-5.

Facilities: ℗ (50yds) ⬜ ♿ (contact for details), shop ⊗ (ex assist dogs) 🚌

GLASGOW

Burrell Collection

2060 Pollokshaws Rd, G43 1AT

☎ 0141 287 2550

🖷 0141 287 2597

e-mail: museums@cls.glasgow.gov.uk

Web: www.glasgowmuseums.com

Dir: *3.5m S of city centre*

Set in Pollok Country Park, this building makes the priceless works of art on display seem almost part of the woodland setting. Shipping magnate Sir William Burrell's main interests were medieval Europe, Oriental art and European paintings. Paintings and stained glass show details of medieval life. Rugs, ceramics and metalwork represent the art of Islam. Strong collection of Chinese and other Oriental ceramics.

Times: *Open all year, Mon-Thu & Sat 10-5, Fri & Sun 11-5. Closed 24-25 & 31 (pm) Dec & 1-2 Jan

Facilities: ℗ (charged) ⬜ 🍴 (licensed) ♿ (wheelchairs, tape guides, lifts), toilets for disabled, shop ⊗ 🚌

GLASGOW

People's Palace & Winter Gardens

Glasgow Green, G40 1AT

☎ 0141 271 2951

🖹 0141 271 2960

e-mail: museums@cls.glasgow.gov.uk

Web: www.glasgowmuseums.com

Dir: *1m SE of city centre*

Glasgow grew from a medieval town located by the Cathedral to the Second City of the British Empire. Trade with the Americas, and later industry, made the city rich. But not everyone shared in the wealth. Visitors can see how an ordinary Glaswegian family lived in a typical one-room 'single end' tenement flat, see Billy Connolly's amazing banana boots, learn to speak Glesga, take a trip 'doon the watter' and visit the Winter Gardens.

Times: *Open all year, Mon-Thu & Sat 10-5, Fri & Sun 11-5. Closed 24-25 & 31 Dec (pm) & 1-2 Jan

Facilities: ℗ (50yds) ⌷ ᪉ (lifts) toilets for disabled, shop, garden centre ⊗ 🚌

GLASGOW

Glasgow Cathedral

Castle St, G4 0QZ

☎ 0141 552 6891

Web: www.historic-scotland.gov.uk

Dir: *M8 junct 15, in centre of Glasgow*

The only Scottish mainland medieval cathedral to have survived the Reformation complete (apart from its western towers). Built during the 13th to 15th centuries over the supposed site of the tomb of St Kentigern. Notable features in this splendid building are the elaborately vaulted crypt, which included an introductory display and collection of carved stones, the stone screen of the early 15th century and the unfinished Blackadder Aisle.

Times: *Open all year, Apr-Sep daily 9.30-6, Sun 1-5; Oct-Mar daily 9.30-4, Sun 1-4. Closed 25-26 Dec & 1-2 Jan.

Facilities: ᪉ (telephone for disabled access details), shop ⊗ 🎌

CITY OF GLASGOW

CITY OF GLASGOW

GLASGOW
Museum of Transport

1 Bunhouse Road, G3 8DP

☎ 0141 287 2720

🗎 0141 287 2692

e-mail: museums@cls.glasgow.gov.uk

Web: www.glasgowmuseums.com

Dir: *1.5m W of city centre*

Visit the Museum of Transport and the first impression is of gleaming metalwork and bright paint. There are cars, caravans, carriages and carts, fire engines, buses, steam locomotives, prams and trams. The museum tells the story of transport by land and sea, with a Glasgow flavour. Visitors can even go window shopping along the Kelvin Street of 1938. Upstairs 250 ship models tell the story of the great days of Clyde shipbuilding.

Times: *Open all year, Mon-Thu & Sat 10-5, Fri & Sun 11-5.

Facilities: 🅿 (charged) 🅟 (100yds) ☕ ♿ (assistance available), toilets for disabled, shop 🚫 (ex assist dogs) 🚌

GLASGOW
McLellan Galleries

270 Sauchiehall Street, G2 3EH

☎ 0141 565 4137

🗎 0141 565 4111

e-mail: museums@cls.glasgow.gov.uk

Web: www.glasgowmuseums.com

Dir: *N side of Sauchiehall St, close to Glasgow School of Art*

The McLellan Galleries first opened in 1854 and featured the personal collection of Glasgow industrialist and coachbuilder Archibald McLellan. With over 1,200 sq metres of top gallery space, the McLellan Galleries provide Glasgow Museums with the opportunity to hold major exhibitions and establish Glasgow as Britain's second art city.

Times: *Open all year, Mon-Thu & Sat 10-5, Fri & Sun 11-5. Closed 24-25 & 31 Dec (pm) & 1-2 Jan

Facilities: 🅟 (500yds) ☕ ♿ (assistance available, lift), toilets for disabled, shop 🚫 🚌

GLASGOW
St Mungo Museum of Religious Life & Art

2 Castle Street, G4 0RH

☎ 0141 553 2557

🖹 0141 552 4744

e-mail: museums@cls.glasgow.gov.uk

Web: www.glasgowmuseums.com

Dir: *1m NE of city centre*

The award-winning St Mungo Museum explores the importance of religion in peoples' everyday lives and art. It aims to promote respect between people of different faiths and of none. Highlights of the collection include the Salvador Dali painting 'Christ of St John of the Cross'. The museum also features stained glass, statues and video footage. Within the grounds is Britain's first Japanese Zen garden.

Times: *Open all year, Mon-Thu & Sat 10-5, Fri & Sun 11-5.

Facilities: ℗ (50yds) ⬆ (licensed) ♿ (taped information & lift), toilets for disabled, shop ⊗ (ex assist dogs) 🚌

GLASGOW
Gallery of Modern Art

Royal Exchange Square, G1 3AH

☎ 0141 229 1996

🖹 0141 204 5316

e-mail: museums@cls.glasgow.gov.uk

Web: www.glasgowmuseums.com

Dir: *just off Buchanan St & close to Central Station & Queen St*

GoMA offers a thought-provoking programme of temporary exhibitions and workshops. It displays work by local and international artists, as well as addressing contemporary social issues through its major bi-annual projects.

Times: *Open all year, Mon-Tue & Sat 10-5, Thu 10-8, Fri & Sun 11-5.

Facilities: ℗ (200yds) ⬆ ♿ toilets for disabled, shop ⊗ (ex assist dogs) 🚌

CITY OF GLASGOW

CITY OF GLASGOW/HIGHLAND

GLASGOW

Glasgow Museums Resource Centre

200 Woodhead Road, South Nitshill Ind Estate, G53 7NN

☎ 0141 276 9300

🖹 0141 276 9305

Web: www.glasgowmuseums.com

Dir: *on S side, close to railway station*

GMRC is the first publicly-accessible store for the city's museum service, offering a behind-the-scenes look at 200,000 treasures held in storage. Please note that access to the stores is by guided tour only. Viewings of a specific object can be arranged, with two weeks prior notice. Activities, tours and talks are held throughout the year - see website or phone for details.

Times: *Open all year Mon-Thu & Sat 10-5, Fri-Sun 11-5. Guided tours for public at 2.30. Access is only by guided tours.

Facilities: 🅿 ♿ toilets for disabled ⊗ (ex assist dogs) 🚌 (please pre-book)

CLAVA CAIRNS

Clava Cairns

☎ 01667 460232

Web: www.historic-scotland.gov.uk

Dir: *6m E of Inverness, signed from B9091*

A well-preserved Bronze Age cemetery complex of passage graves, ring cairns, kerb cairn and standing stones in a beautiful setting. In addition, the remains of a chapel of unknown date can be seen at this site.

Times: *Open at all reasonable times.

Facilities: 🅿 ⊗ 🚌 🏴

FORT WILLIAM
Inverlochy Castle

PH33 6SN

Web: www.historic-scotland.gov.uk

Dir: *2m NE of Fort William, off A82*

A fine well-preserved 13th-century castle of the Comyn family; in the form of a square, with round towers at the corners. The largest tower was the donjon or keep. This is one of Scotland's earliest castles.

Times: *Open at all reasonable times.

Facilities: 🅿 ⊗ 🚾

KINGUSSIE
Ruthven Barracks

☎ 01667 460232

Web: www.historic-scotland.gov.uk

Dir: *1m SE from Kingussie, signed from A9 and A86*

An infantry barracks erected in 1719 following the Jacobite rising of 1715, with two ranges of quarters and a stable block. Captured and burnt by Prince Charles Edward Stuart's army in 1746.

Times: *Open at any reasonable time.

Facilities: 🅿 ⊗ 🚾

HIGHLAND

HIGHLAND

ROSEMARKIE
Groam House Museum

High Street, IV10 8UF

☎ 01381 620961 & 01463 811883

▤ 01381 621730

e-mail: groamhouse@ecosse.net

Dir: *off A9 at Tore onto A832*

Opened in 1980, this community-based museum explores the history, culture and crafts of the mysterious Picts, who faded from history over a thousand years ago. Visitors can see the Rosemarkie Stones, large slabs that show Pictish carvings; paintings, a replica Pictish harp, and a collection of photographs of Pictish stones all over the country. The museum holds the George Bain Collection of Celtic art for the Scottish Nation. Annual exhibitions, often loans from other museums.

Times: Open Etr week, daily 2-4.30; May-Oct, Mon-Sat, 10-5, Sun 2-4.30; Apr, Sat-Sun 2-4.30. Nov-mid Dec, Sat-Sun 2-4

Facilities: ❷ ℗ (50yds) ♿ (key for disabled public toilets), shop ⊗ (ex assist dogs) 🚍 (40 people max)

WICK
Castle of Old Wick

☎ 01667 460232

Web: www.historic-scotland.gov.uk

Dir: *1m S on Shore Rd*

The ruin of the best-preserved Norse castle in Scotland. Dating from the 12th-century this spectacular site is on a spine of rock projecting into the sea, between two deep, narrow gullies. Visitors must take great care and wear sensible shoes.

Times: *Open at all reasonable times.

Facilities: ⊗ 🅿

GREENOCK
McLean Museum & Art Gallery

15 Kelly Street, PA16 8JX

☎ 01475 715624

🖷 01475 715626

e-mail: museum@inverclyde.gov.uk

Web: www.inverclyde.gov.uk/museum_gallery

Dir: *close to Greenock West Railway Station and Greenock Bus Station*

James Watt was born in Greenock, and various exhibits connected with him are shown. The museum also has an art collection, and displays on shipping, local and natural history, Egyptology and ethnography.

Times: *Open all year, Mon-Sat 10-5. Closed local & national PHs.

Facilities: ℗ (200yds) ♿ (induction loop) toilets for disabled, shop ⊗ (ex assist dogs) 🚌

EAST LINTON
Hailes Castle

Web: www.historic-scotland.gov.uk

Dir: *1.5m SW of East Linton on A1*

A beautiful sited ruin incorporating a fortified manor of 13th-century date, extended in the 14th and 15th centuries. There are two vaulted pit-prisons.

Times: *Open at all reasonable times.

Facilities: ℗ ⌹ ⊗ 🚩

EAST LOTHIAN/MIDLOTHIAN

PRESTONPANS
Prestongrange Museum
Prestongrange
☎ 0131 653 2904
🖹 01620 828201
e-mail: elms@eastlothian.gov.uk
Web: www.eastlothian.gov.uk/museums
Dir: *on B1348*

The oldest documented coal mining site in Scotland, with 800 years of history, this museum shows a Cornish Beam Engine and on-site evidence of associated industries such as brickmaking and pottery. It is located next to a 16th-century customs port. Special Events - weekend events for families and children in July/August.

Times: *Open end Mar-mid Oct, daily 11-4.
Facilities: ❷ ⏰ 🍴 ♿ (grounds partly accessible) toilets for disabled, shop, tours available, audio commentaries available ⊗ (ex assist dogs) 🚌

PENICUIK
Edinburgh Crystal Visitor Centre
Eastfield, EH26 8HB
☎ 01968 675128
🖹 01968 673622
e-mail: visitorcentre@edinburgh-crystal.co.uk
Web: www.edinburgh-crystal.com
Dir: *Follow brown Thistle signs from Edinburgh City Bypass and A701/703*

Watch skilled craftsmen as they take molten crystal and turn it into intricately decorated glassware. Not only can you talk to the craftsmen themselves but there is also video footage, story boards, artefacts and audio listening posts to help you understand the 300-year-old history of glassmaking.

Times: Open Mon-Sat 10-5, Sun 11-5. Closed 25-26 Dec and 1-2 Jan.
Facilities: ❷ Ⓟ 100yds ⏰ 🍴 (licensed) 🍴 ♿ (ramp to first floor), toilets for disabled (toilet on ground floor), shop ⊗ (ex assist dogs) 🚌 (pre-book catering requirements)

BALLINDALLOCH
The Glenlivet Distillery

Glenlivet, AB37 9DB

☎ 01340 821720

🖹 01340 821718

e-mail: betty.munro@chivas.com

Web: www.theglenlivet.com

Dir: *10m N of Tomintoul, off B9008*

The visitor centre includes a guided tour of the whisky production facilities and a chance to see inside the vast bonded warehouses where the spirit matures. The new multimedia exhibition and interactive presentations communicate the unique history, and traditions of Glenlivet Scotch Whisky.

Times: Open 2 Apr-2 Nov.

Facilities: 🅿 (no overnight parking) 🍽 (licensed) ♿ (cafeteria, lift to exhibition) toilets for disabled (one toilet available) shop, tours available, audio commentaries available 🚫 (ex assist dogs) 🚌 (pre-booking preferred)

DUFFTOWN
Glenfiddich Distillery

Keith, AB55 4DH

☎ 01340 820373

🖹 01340 822083

Web: www.glenfiddich.com

Dir: *N of town, off A941*

Set close to Balvenie Castle, the distillery was founded in 1887 by William Grant and has stayed in the hands of the family ever since. Visitors can see the whisky-making process in its various stages, including bottling, and then sample the finished product.

Times: *Open all year Mon-Fri 9.30-4.30, also Etr-mid Oct, Sat 9.30-4.30, Sun 12-4.30. Closed Xmas & New Year

Facilities: 🅿 (only in designated areas) 🍽 (licensed) ⛺ ♿ (ramp access to production area & warehouse gallery) toilets for disabled, shop, tours available, audio commentaries available 🚫 (ex assist dogs) 🚌 (must pre-book)

MORAY

MORAY

DUFFUS
Duffus Castle
☎ 01667 460232
Web: www.historic-scotland.gov.uk
Dir: *5m NW of Elgin on B9012 to Burghead*
One of the finest examples of a motte and bailey castle in Scotland with a later, very fine, stone hall house and curtain wall. The original seat of the Moray family.
Times: *Open at all reasonable times.
Facilities: ❷ ⊗ ✠

ELGIN
Pluscarden Abbey
IV30 8UA
☎ 01343 890257
🖹 01343 890258
e-mail: monks@pluscardenabbey.org
Web: www.pluscardenabbey.org
Dir: *6m SW of Elgin on unclass road*
The original monastery was founded in 1230 by King Alexander II for monks of the Valliscaulian order from Burgundy. Monastic life was abandoned after the Reformation and only recommenced in 1948. Today there are about two dozen monks who lead a life of prayer, study and manual work. The services in the Abbey church are sung in Latin with Gregorian chant and are open to the public.
Times: Open all year, daily 4.45am-8.30pm
Facilities: ℗ (100yds) ♿ (induction loop, ramps to shop, garden partially accessible), toilets for disabled (unisex, grab rail) shop, tours available ⊗ (ex assist dogs) 🚌 (park in designated area only)

FOCHABERS

Baxters Highland Village

IV32 7LD

☎ 01343 820666

🖨 01343 821790

e-mail: highland.village@baxters.co.uk

Web: www.baxters.com

Dir: *1m W of Fochabers on A96*

The Baxters food firm started here over 130 years ago and now sells its products in over 60 countries. Visitors can see the shop where the story began, watch an audio-visual display, and visit five shops. See the great hall, audio-visual theatre and cooking theatre. A food tasting area is open to visitors.

Times: *Open all year daily, Jan-Mar 10-5; Apr-Dec 9-5.30.

Facilities: ❷ 🍴 (licensed) 🚻 ♿ (parking facilities) toilets for disabled, shop ⊗ (ex assist dogs) 🚌 (pre-booking required)

FORRES

Sueno's Stone

☎ 01667 460232

Web: www.historic-scotland.gov.uk

Dir: *E end of Forres, off A96*

The most remarkable sculptured monument in Britain, probably a cenotaph, standing over 20 feet high and dating back to the end of the first millennium AD. Covered by a protective glass enclosure.

Times: *Open at all reasonable times.

Facilities: ❷ ⊗ 🚩

MORAY

MORAY

ROTHES
Glen Grant Distillery

AB38 7BS

☎ 01340 832118

🖷 01340 832104

e-mail: jennifer.robertson@glengrant.com

Dir: *on A941 Elgin-Rothes road*

Founded in 1840 in a sheltered glen by the two Grant brothers. Discover the secrets of the distillery, including the delightful Victorian garden originally created by Major Grant, and now restored to its former glory, where you can enjoy a dram.

Times: *Open Apr-3 Nov, Mon-Sat, 9.30-5, Sun, 12-5.

Facilities: 𝗣 ♿ (reception centre & still house), toilets for disabled (facilities available in reception/shop) shop, tours available ⊗ (ex assist dogs) 🚌 (pre-booking advisable max 50)

SPEY BAY
The WDCS Wildlife Centre

Fochabers, IV32 7PJ

☎ 01343 829109

🖷 01343 829065

e-mail: enquiries@mfwc.co.uk

Web: www.mfwc.co.uk

Dir: *off A96 onto B9014 at Fochabers, follow road approx 5m to village of Spey Bay. Turn left at Spey Bay Hotel and follow road for 500yds*

The centre, owned and operated by the Whale and Dolphin Conservation Society, lies at the mouth of the River Spey and is housed in a former salmon fishing station, built in 1768. There is a free exhibition about the Moray Firth dolphins and the wildlife of Spey Bay. Visitors can browse through a well-stocked gift shop and enjoy refreshments in the cosy tea room.

Times: *Open Apr-Oct 10.30-5. Check for winter opening times

Facilities: 𝗣 (20yds) ⬛ 🍴 ♿ toilets for disabled, shop, tours available ⊗ (ex assist dogs) 🚌 (must pre-book)

TOMINTOUL

Tomintoul Museum

The Square, AB37 9ET

☎ 01309 673701

🖹 01309 673701

e-mail: museums@moray.gov.uk/museums

Web: www.moray.gov.uk

Dir: *on A939, 13m E of Grantown*

Situated in one of the highest villages in Britain, the museum features a reconstructed crofter's kitchen and smiddy, with other displays on the local wildlife, the story of Tomintoul, and the local skiing industry.

Times: Open: Mar-May, Mon-Fri, 9.30-12 and 2-4. Jun-Aug, Mon-Sat, 9.30-12 and 2-4.30. Sep, Mon-Sat, 9.30-12 and 2-4. Oct, Mon-Fri, 9.30-12 and 2-4. Closed May Day and Good Fri.

Facilities: 🅿 Ⓟ (200yds) 🚻 ♿ (induction loop and sound commentaries) shop, tours available, audio commentaries available ⊗ (ex assist dogs) 🚌 (pre-booking preferred)

BIRSAY

Earl's Palace

KW15 1PD

☎ 01856 721205 & 841815

Web: www.historic-scotland.gov.uk

Dir: *on A966*

The gaunt remains of the residence of the 16th-century Earl of Orkney, constructed round a courtyard.

Times: *Open at all reasonable times.

Facilities: ⊗ 🚩

MORAY/ORKNEY

ORKNEY

DOUNBY
Click Mill

☎ 01856 841815

Web: www.historic-scotland.gov.uk

Dir: *2.5m from Dounby on B905*

The last surviving horizontal water mill in Orkney, of a type well represented in Shetland and Lewis. The mill is in working condition and visitors should wear sensible footwear.

Times: *Open at all reasonable times.

Facilities: 🏛

FINSTOWN
Stones of Stenness Circle and Henge

☎ 01856 841815

Web: www.historic-scotland.gov.uk

Dir: *5m NE of Stromness on B9055*

Dating back to the second millennium BC, the remains of this stone circle are near the Ring of Brogar - a splendid circle of upright stones surrounded by a ditch.

Times: *Open at any reasonable time.

Facilities: 🅿 🚌 🏛

HARRAY

Corrigall Farm & Kirbuster Museum

KW17 2JR

☎ 01856 771411 & 771268

🖹 01856 874615

The museum consists of two Orkney farmhouses with outbuildings. Kirbuster (Birsay) has the last surviving example of a 'Firehoose' with its central hearth; Corrigall (Harray) represents an improved farmhouse and steading of the late 1800s.

Times: *Open Mar-Oct, Mon-Sat 10.30-1 & 2-5, Sun 2-7.

Facilities: 🅿 Ⓟ (at museum) 🍴 ♿ toilets for disabled, shop, tours available Ⓧ (ex assist dogs) 🚌

KIRKWALL

The Orkney Museum

Broad St, KW15 1DH

☎ 01856 87355

🖹 01856 873535

e-mail: museum@orkney.gov.uk

Web: www.orkneyheritage.com

Dir: *town centre*

One of the finest vernacular town houses in Scotland, this 16th-century building now contains a museum of Orkney history, including the islands' fascinating archaeology.

Times: *Open, Oct-Mar Mon-Sat, 10.30-12.30 & 1.30-5, Apr-Sep, 10.30-5 Mon-Sat.

Facilities: Ⓟ (50yds) ♿ toilets for disabled, shop Ⓧ (ex assist dogs) 🚌

ORKNEY

ORKNEY

KIRKWALL
Scapa Flow Visitor Centre & Museum
Lyness, Hoy

☎ 01856 791300

🖹 01856 871560

e-mail: museum@orkney.gov.uk

Web: www.orkneyheritage.com

Dir: *on A964 to Houton, ferry crossing takes 30 mins, visitors centre 2 mins from ferry terminal*

Also known as the Lyness Interpretation Centre, this fascinating museum is home to a large collection of military equipment used in the defence of the Orkneys during the First and Second World Wars. There are also guns salvaged from the German ships scuppered in WWII. Visitors arrive at the island after a short boat trip from the Orkney mainland.

Times: *Open all year: Mon-Fri 9-4.30 (mid May-Oct also Sat, Sun 10.30-3.30)

Facilities: ℗ ⊡ ♿ toilets for disabled, shop, tours available ⊗ (ex assist dogs) 🚌

STROMNESS
Pier Arts Centre
KW16 3AA

☎ 01856 850209

🖹 01856 851462

e-mail: info@pierartscentre.com

Web: www.pierartscentre.com

A permanent collection of modern art and sculpture including works by Barbara Hepworth and Ben Nicholson, given to Orkney by the late Margaret Gardiner. These works are housed in a landmark 18th-century building that has served as merchants' offices, a cooperage, stores and private lodgings.

Times: Open from Spring, Tues-Sat.

Facilities: ℗ (100yds) ♿ toilets for disabled, shop ⊗ (ex assist dogs) 🚌

WESTRAY
Noltland Castle
☎ 01856 841815
Web: www.historic-scotland.gov.uk
Dir: *1m W of Pierowall village*

A fine, ruined Z-plan tower, built between 1560 and 1573 but never completed. The tower is remarkable for its large number of gun loops and impressive staircase.

Times: *Open 11 Jun-Sep, daily 9.30-6.30.

Facilities: ⊗ ▉

DUNKELD
The Ell Shop & Little Houses
The Cross, PH8 0AN
☎ 01350 727460
e-mail: dunkeld@nts.org.uk
Web: www.nts.org.uk
Dir: *off A9, 15m N of Perth*

The National Trust owns two rows of 20 houses in Dunkeld, and has preserved their 17th/18th-century character. They are not open to the public, but there is a display and audio-visual show in the Information Centre.

Times: *Open Ell Shop mid Mar-Sep, Mon-Sat, 10-5.30, Sun 12.30-5.30. Oct-mid Dec, Mon-Sat 10-4.30, Sun 12.30-4.30.

Facilities: ℗ (300yds) ♿ toilets for disabled, shop ⊗ 🚌 ☕

ORKNEY/PERTH & KINROSS

PERTH & KINROSS

KILLIECRANKIE
Killiecrankie Visitor Centre

NTS Visitor Centre, Pitlochry, PH16 5LG

☎ 01796 473233

🖷 01796 473233

e-mail: killiecrankie@nts.org.uk

Web: www.nts.org.uk

Dir: *3m N of Pitlochry on B8079*

The visitor centre features an exhibition on the battle of 1689, when the Jacobite army routed the English, although the Jacobite leader, 'Bonnie Dundee', was mortally wounded in the attack. The wooded gorge is a notable beauty spot, admired by Queen Victoria, and there are some splendid walks.

Times: *Visitor Centre: Open Apr-Jun & Sep-Oct, daily 10-5.30, Jul & Aug, daily 9.30-6. Site: open all year daily. Times may change for 2007 please telephone or check website

Facilities: ❷ ⌨ 🛱 ♿ (visitor centre only) toilets for disabled, shop 🚌 (pre-booking required) ♨

MILNATHORT
Burleigh Castle

KY13 7XZ

Web: www.historic-scotland.gov.uk

Dir: *0.5m E of Milnathort on A911*

The roofless but otherwise complete ruin of a tower house of about 1500, with a section of defensive barmkin wall and a remarkable corner tower with a square cap-house corbelled out. This castle was often visited by James IV.

Times: *Open summer only. Keys available locally, telephone 01786 45000.

Facilities: ⊗ 🚩

PERTH
Perth Museum & Art Gallery

78 George Street, PH1 5LB

☎ 01738 632488

🖷 01738 443505

e-mail: museum@pkc.gov.uk

Web: www.pkc.gov.uk

Dir: *in town centre, adjacent to Perth Concert Hall*

Visit Perth Museum and Art Gallery for a fascinating look into Perthshire throughout the ages. Collections cover silver, glass, art, natural history, archaeology and human history.

Times: Open all year, Mon-Sat 10-5. Sun. 1-4.30, May-Sep. Closed Xmas-New Year.

Facilities: Ⓟ (800yds) (pay and display) ♿ (ramp, lifts, induction loops) toilets for disabled (male and female facilities available), shop ⊗ (ex assist dogs) 🚌

PERTH
Caithness Glass Factory & Visitor Centre

Inveralmond, PH1 3TZ

☎ 01738 492320

🖷 01738 492300

e-mail: visitor@caithnessglass.co.uk

Web: www.caithnessglass.co.uk

Dir: *on Perth Western Bypass, A9, at Inveralmond Roundabout*

All aspects of paperweight-making can be seen from the purpose-built viewing galleries. There are talks in the glasshouse regularly throughout the day from Monday to Friday. There is a factory shop, a best shop, play area and information centre with internet access.

Times: *Open all year, Factory shop & restaurant, Mon-Sat 9-5, Sun 10-5 (Dec-Feb 12-5). Glassmaking Mon-Sun 9-4.30.

Facilities: Ⓟ ⑪ (licensed) ㇰ ♿ (wheelchair available) toilets for disabled, shop, tours available, audio commentaries available ⊗ (ex assist dogs) 🚌

PERTH & KINROSS

PERTH & KINROSS

PITLOCHRY
Edradour Distillery
PH16 5JP
☎ 01796 472095
🖷 01796 472002
Web: www.edradour.co.uk
Dir: *2.5m E of Pitlochry on A924*
It was in 1825 that a group of local farmers founded Edradour, naming it after the bubbling burn that runs through it. It is Scotland's smallest distillery and is virtually unchanged since Victorian times. Have a dram of whisky while watching an audio-visual in the malt barn and then take a guided tour of the distillery.
Times: *Open Jan-Feb, Mon-Sat 10-5, Sun 12.4; Mar-Oct Mon-Sat 9.30-6, Sun 11.30-6; Nov-Dec, Mon-Sat 9.30-5, Sun 12-5. (Last tour 1hr before close, private tours arranged for a fee).
Facilities: ❷ ♿ toilets for disabled, wide doors, safety rail, low wash basin, shop ⊗ (ex assist dogs) 🚌 (pre-booking required)

QUEEN'S VIEW
Queen's View Visitor Centre
Strathtummel, Pitlochry, PH16 5NR
☎ 01350 727284
🖷 01350 728635
e-mail: peter.fullarton@forestry.gsi.gov.uk
Web: www.forestry.gov.uk
Dir: *7m W of Pitlochry on B8019*
Queen Victoria admired the view on a visit here in 1866; it is possibly one of the most famous views in Scotland. The area, in the heart of the Tay Forest Park, has a variety of woodlands that visitors can walk or cycle in.
Times: *Open Apr-Nov, daily 10-6.
Facilities: ❷ (charged) ⊑ 🪑 ♿ toilets for disabled, shop 🚌

PAISLEY
Coats Observatory

49 Oakshaw Street West, PA1 2DE

☎ 0141 889 2013

🖹 0141 889 9240

e-mail: museums.els@renfrewshire.gov.uk

Web: www.renfrewshire.gov.uk

Dir: *M8 junct 27, follow signs to town centre until Gordon St (A761). Left onto Causeyside St, left onto New St then left onto High St*

The Observatory, funded by Thomas Coats and designed by John Honeyman, was opened in 1883. It houses a 5-inch telescope under the dome at the top. Weather recording activities have been carried out here since 1884. There is also earthquake-measuring equipment. There are displays on the solar system, earthquakes and the telescope.

Times: *Open all year, Tue-Sat 10-5, Sun 2-5. Last entry 15 minutes before closing.

Facilities: Ⓟ (150yds) (meters/limited street parking) tours available ⊗ (ex assist dogs) 🚌 (max 40)

PAISLEY
Paisley Museum & Art Galleries

High Street, PA1 2BA

☎ 0141 889 3151

🖹 0141 889 9240

e-mail: museums.els@renfrewshire

Web: www.renfrewshire.gov.uk

Dir: *M8 junct 27 (A741), rdbt 2nd exit (A761-town centre). At lights take left lane towards Kilbride. Onto Gordon St, right onto Causeyside St, left onto New St, left onto High St*

Pride of place here is given to a world-famous collection of Paisley shawls. Other collections illustrate local industrial and natural history, while the emphasis of the art gallery is on 19th-century Scottish artists and an important studio ceramics collection.

Times: *Open all year, Tue-Sat 10-5, Sun 2-5. BHs 10-5.

Facilities: Ⓟ (330yds) ♿ (parking on site) toilets for disabled, shop, tours available ⊗ (ex assist dogs) 🚌 (max 80)

RENFREWSHIRE

KELSO
Kelso Abbey
☎ 0131 668 8800
Web: www.historic-scotland.gov.uk
Founded by David I in 1128 and probably the greatest of the four famous Border abbeys, Kelso became extremely wealthy and acquired extensive lands. In 1545 it served as a fortress when the town was attacked by the Earl of Hertford, but now only fragments of the once-imposing abbey church give any clue to its long history.
Times: *Open at any reasonable time.
Facilities: & all parts accessible 🚌 🏳

SELKIRK
Halliwells House Museum
Halliwells Close, Market Place, TD7 4BC
☎ 01750 20096
📄 01750 23282
e-mail: museums@scotborders.gov.uk
Dir: *off A7 in town centre*
A row of late 18th-century town cottages converted into a museum. Displays recreate the building's former use as an ironmonger's shop and home, and tell the story of the Royal Burgh of Selkirk. The Robson Gallery hosts a programme of contemporary art and craft exhibitions.
Times: *Open Apr-Sep, Mon-Sat 10-5, Sun 10-12; Jul-Aug, Mon-Sat 10-5.30, Sun 10-12; Oct, Mon-Sat 10-4.
Facilities: 🅿 (charged) 🅿 & (lift to first floor, large print, interpretation) toilets for disabled (located outside the museum), shop ⊗ (ex assist dogs) 🚌 (24hrs notice preferred)

SELKIRK
Sir Walter Scott's Courtroom

Market Place, TD7 4BT

☎ 01750 20096

🖹 01750 23282

e-mail: museums@scotborders.gov.uk

Dir: *on A7 in town centre*

Built in 1803-4 as a sheriff court and town hall this is where the famous novelist, Sir Walter Scott dispensed justice when he was Sheriff of Selkirkshire from 1804-1832. Displays tell of Scott's time as Sheriff, and of his place as a novelist as well as those of his contemporaries, writer, James Hogg and the explorer, Mungo Park.

Times: *Open Apr-Sep, Mon-Fri 10-4, Sat 10-2; May-Aug also Sun 10-2; Oct, Mon-Sat 1-4.

Facilities: ℗ (100yds) (30min on street, car park for 2hrs), toilets for disabled (1 fully equipped cubicle), shop ⊗ (ex assist dogs) 🚌 (pre-booking preferred)

LERWICK
Clickimin

ZE1 0QX

☎ 01466 793191

Web: www.historic-scotland.gov.uk

Dir: *1m SW of Lerwick on A970*

The remains of a prehistoric settlement that was fortified at the beginning of the Iron Age with a stone-built fort. The site was occupied for over 1000 years. The remains include a partially demolished broch (round tower) which still stands to a height of 17ft.

Times: *Open at all reasonable times.

Facilities: 🏛

SCOTTISH BORDERS/SHETLAND

SHETLAND

LERWICK
Fort Charlotte
ZE1 0JN
☎ 01466 793191
Web: www.historic-scotland.gov.uk
Dir: *in centre of Lerwick*
A five-sided artillery fort with bastions projecting from each corner. The walls are high and massive. It was built in 1665 to protect the Sound of Bressay from the Dutch, but taken by them and burned in 1673. It was rebuilt in 1781.
Times: *Open at all reasonable times. Key available locally.
Facilities: ∎

LERWICK
Shetland Museum
Hay's Dock
☎ 01595 695057
🖷 01595 696729
e-mail: shetland.museum@sic.shetland.gov.uk
Web: www.shetland-museum.org.uk
Please note the Museum will re-open as the New Shetland Museum and Archives in 2007. The museum sits alongside Hay's Dock, the last remaining part of old Lerwick waterfront.
Times: Re-launch of museum. Please telephone for details of opening times and admission prices.
Facilities: Please telephone for details of the new facilities

MOUSA ISLAND
Mousa Broch

☎ 01466 793191

Web: www.historic-scotland.gov.uk

Dir: *accessible by boat from Sandwick*

This broch is the best-preserved example of an Iron Age drystone tower in Scotland. The tower is nearly complete and rises to a height of 40ft. The outer and inner walls both contain staircases that may be climbed to the parapet.

Times: *Open at all reasonable time.

Facilities: ◪

SCALLOWAY
Scalloway Castle

ZE1 0TP

☎ 01466 793191

Web: www.historic-scotland.gov.uk

Dir: *6m from Lerwick on A970*

The ruins of a castle designed on the medieval two-step plan. The castle was actually built in 1600 by Patrick Stewart, Earl of Orkney. When the Earl, who was renowned for his cruelty, was executed in 1615, the castle fell into disuse.

Times: *Open at all reasonable time.

Facilities: ⓟ ◪

SHETLAND

NORTH LANARKSHIRE/SOUTH LANARKSHIRE

MOTHERWELL
Motherwell Heritage Centre
High Rd, ML1 3HU
☎ 01698 251000
🖹 01698 268867
e-mail: museums@northlan.gov.uk
Web: www.nlcmuseums.bravehost.com
Dir: *A723 for town centre. Left at top of hill, after pedestrian crossing*

Audio-visual experience, 'Technopolis', traces the history of the area from Roman times to the rise of 19th-century industry and the post-industrial era. Also a viewing tower, exhibition gallery and family history research facilities.

Times: *Open all year Wed-Sat 10-5 (Thu 10-7), Sun 12-5. Closed Mon & Tue, ex BHs. Local studies library closed Sun

Facilities: 🅿 & (lifts, audio info & Braille buttons) toilets for disabled (wheelchair accessible) shop, tours available ⊗ (ex assist dogs) 🚌

HAMILTON
Low Parks Museum
129 Muir Street, ML3 6BJ
☎ 01698 328232
🖹 01698 328412
e-mail: lowparksmuseum@southlanarkshire.gov.uk
Web: www.southlanarkshire.gov.uk
Dir: *off M74 junct 6, by Asda Superstore*

The museum tells the story of both South Lanarkshire and The Cameronians (Scottish Rifles). The Cameronians were unique as they were the only Scottish rifle regiment, and the museum details their fascinating history from 1689 to 1968. Housed in the town's oldest building, dating from 1696, the museum also features a restored 18th-century assembly room and exhibitions on Hamilton Palace and The Covenanters.

Times: Open all year, daily, Mon-Sat 10-5, Sun 12-5

Facilities: 🅿 & toilets for disabled, 2 toilets on ground floor, shop ⊗ (ex assist dogs) 🚌 (pre-booking preferred)

HAMILTON
Chatelherault Country Park

Ferniegair, ML3 7UE

☎ 01698 426213

🖷 01698 421532

e-mail: phyllis.crosbie@southlanarkshire.gov.uk

Web: www.southlanarkshire.gov.uk

Dir: *2.5km SE of Hamilton on A72 Hamilton-Larkhall/Lanark Clyde Valley tourist route*

Designed as a hunting lodge by William Adam in 1732, Chatelherault, built of unusual pink sandstone, has been described as a gem of Scottish architecture. Situated close to the motorway, there is a shop and adventure playground. Also a herd of white Cadzow cattle.

Times: Visitor Centre, open all year, Mon-Sat 10-5, Sun 12-5. House closed all day Fri & Sat.

Facilities: ❷ (no overnight parking) ⌷ ㅐ ㄥ (ramps, parking, large print guide), toilets for disabled (in visitor centre), shop, garden centre, tours available ⊗ (ex in grounds & assist dogs) 🚌 (prefer pre-booking)

BANNOCKBURN
Bannockburn Heritage Centre

Glasgow Road, FK7 0LJ

☎ 01786 812664

🖷 01786 810892

Web: www.nts.org.uk

Dir: *2m S of Stirling off M80/M9 junct 9*

The Heritage Centre stands close to what is traditionally believed to have been Robert the Bruce's command post before the 1314 Battle of Bannockburn, a famous victory for the Scots and a turning point in Scottish history.

Times: *Site open all year, daily. Heritage Centre Apr-Oct, daily 10-5.30; Feb-Mar & Nov-24 Dec, daily 10.30-4. (Last audio-visual show 30 mins before closing).

Facilities: ❷ (charged) ⌷ ㄥ (Induction loop), toilets for disabled, shop ⊗ (ex site) 🚌 (pre-booking required) ♥

STIRLING/WESTERN ISLES

STIRLING

Mar's Wark

Broad Street, FK8 1EE

Web: www.historic-scotland.gov.uk

A remarkable Renaissance mansion built by the Earl of Mar, Regent for James VI in 1570 and later used as the town workhouse. It was never completed and now the façade can be seen.

Times: *Open all reasonable times.

Facilities: ⊗ ▮

CARLOWAY

Dun Carloway Broch

Web: www.historic-scotland.gov.uk

Dir: *1.5m S of Carloway on A858*

Brochs are late-prehistoric circular stone towers, and their origins are mysterious. One of the best examples can be seen at Dun Carloway, where the tower still stands about 30ft high.

Times: *Open at all reasonable times.

Facilities: ℗ 🚌 ▮

BRIDGEND
Newcastle
☎ 01656 659515

Web: www.cadw.wales.gov.uk

The small castle dates back to the 12th century. It is ruined, but a rectangular tower, a richly carved Norman gateway and massive curtain walls enclosing a polygonal courtyard can still be seen.

Times: *Open - accessible throughout the year. Key keeper arrangement.

Facilities: Ⓟ ⊗ 🚌 ⊕

COITY
Coity Castle
CF35 6BG

☎ 01656 652021

Web: www.cadw.wales.gov.uk

Dir: *2m NE of Bridgend, off A4061*

A 12th to 16th-century stronghold, with a hall, chapel and the remains of a square keep.

Times: *Open all year, at all times. Key keeper arrangement.

Facilities: Ⓟ ⊗ 🚌 ⊕

CARDIFF

CARDIFF
National Museum Cardiff
Cathays Park, CF10 3NP
☎ 029 2039 7951
🖹 029 2037 3219
e-mail: post@museumwales.ac.uk
Web: www.museumwales.a.uk
Dir: *in Civic Centre, 5 mins walk from city centre & 20 mins walk from bus & train station*

'The Evolution of Wales' exhibition is a spectacular 4600-million year journey, tracing the world from beginning of time and the development of Wales. Displays of Bronze Age gold, early Christian monuments, Celtic treasures, and fossils. French Impressionist paintings sit alongside works of Welsh artists.
Times: *Open all year, Tue-Sun 10-5. Closed Mon (ex BHs) & 24-26 Dec.
Facilities: 🅿 (charged) 🍴 (licensed) ♿ (wheelchair available, Tel 029 2057 3509 for access guide), toilets for disabled, shop ⊗ (ex assist dogs) 🚌 (pre-booking required)

ST FAGANS
St Fagans:
National History Museum
Cardiff, CF5 6XB
☎ 029 2057 3500
🖹 029 2057 3490
e-mail: post@nmgw.ac.uk
Web: www.nmgw.ac.uk
Dir: *4m W of Cardiff on A4232. From M4 junct 33 follow brown signs*

A stroll around the indoor galleries and 100 acres of beautiful grounds give a fascinating insight into how people in Wales have lived since Celtic times. You can see people practising the traditional means of earning a living and the animals they kept.
Times: *Open all year daily, 10-5. Closed 24-26 Dec.
Facilities: 🅿 (charged) 🍴 (licensed) 🚐♿ (wheelchairs, motorised buggy-must pre-book), toilets for disabled, shop ⊗ (ex in grounds if on lead) 🚌 (pre-booking required)

ABERGWILI
Carmarthenshire County Museum

Carmarthen, SA31 2JG

☎ 01267 228696

🖺 01267 223830

e-mail: museums@carmarthenshire.gov.uk

Web: www.carmarthenshire.gov.uk/

Dir: *2m E of Carmarthen, just off A40, at Abergwili rdbt*

Housed in the old palace of the Bishop of St David's and set in seven acres of grounds, the museum offers a wide range of local subjects to explore, from geology and prehistory to butter making, Welsh furniture and folk art. Temporary exhibitions are held.

Times: Open all year, Mon-Sat 10-4.30. Closed Xmas-New Year

Facilities: ❷ 🖵 🎮 ♿ (lift), toilets for disabled, shop ⊗ (ex assist dogs) 🚌 (advance booking preferred)

DRE-FACH FELINDRE
National Wool Museum

Llandysul, SA44 5UP

☎ 01559 370929

🖺 01559 371592

Web: www.museumwales.ac.uk

Dir: *16m W of Carmarthen off A484, 4m E of Newcastle Emlyn*

The museum is housed in the former Cambrian Mills and has a comprehensive display tracing the evolution of the industry from its beginnings to the present day. Demonstrations of the fleece to fabric process are given on 19th-century textile machinery.

Times: Open Apr-Sep, daily 10-5; Oct-Mar, Tue-Sat 10-5. Closed Xmas.

Facilities: ❷ ❷ 🖵 🎮 ♿ (wheelchair access to ground floor & ample seating) toilets for disabled, shop ⊗ (ex assist dogs) 🚌 (prior notification essential)

CARMARTHENSHIRE

CARMARTHENSHIRE

DRYSLWYN
Dryslwyn Castle

☎ 029 2050 0200

Web: www.cadw.wales.gov.uk

Dir: *on B4279*

The ruined 13th-century castle was a stronghold of the native Welsh. It stands on a lofty mound, and was important in the struggles between English and Welsh. It is gradually being uncovered by excavation.

Times: *Open-entrance by arrangement with Dryslwyn Farm.

Facilities: 🅿 ⊗ 🚌 ✛

KIDWELLY
Kidwelly Industrial Museum

Broadford, SA17 4LW

☎ 01554 891078

Dir: *signed from Kidwelly by-pass & town*

Two of the great industries of Wales are represented in this museum: tinplate and coal mining. The original buildings and machinery of the Kidwelly tinplate works, where tinplate was hand made, are now on display to the public. There is also an exhibition of coal mining with pit-head gear and a winding engine, while the more general history of the area is shown in a separate exhibition.

Times: *Open Etr, Jun-Sep, BH wknds, Mon-Fri 10-5, Sat-Sun 12-5. Last admission 4. Other times by arrangement for parties only.

Facilities: 🅿 ⊐ 🎪 ♿ (ramps on entrances), toilets for disabled, shop, tours available 🚌

LLANSTEFFAN
Llansteffan Castle

☎ 01267 241756

Web: www.cadw.wales.gov.uk

Dir: *off B4312*

The ruins of this 11th to 13th-century stronghold stand majestically on the west side of the Towy estuary.

Times: *Open - access throughout the year.

Facilities: ⊗ 🚌 ⊕

CERRIGYDRUDION
Llyn Brenig Visitor Centre

Corwen, LL21 9TT

☎ 01490 420463

🖷 01490 420694

e-mail: llyn.brenig@dwrcymru.com

Web: www.dwrcymru.com

Dir: *on B4501 between Denbigh & Cerrigydrudion*

The 1800-acre estate has a unique archaeological trail and round-the-lake walk of 10 miles. A hide is available and disabled anglers are catered for with a specially adapted fishing boat and an annual open day. The centre has an exhibition on archaeology, history and conservation and an audio-visual programme.

Times: Open mid Mar-Oct, daily 9-5.

Facilities: ❷ (charged) ⊑ 🛏 ♿ (boats for disabled & fishing open days) toilets for disabled, shop ⊗ (ex assist dogs) 🚌 (pre-booking preferred)

CARMARTHENSHIRE/CONWY

CONWY

LLANRWST
Gwydyr Uchaf Chapel
☎ 01492 640578
Web: www.cadw.wales.gov.uk
Dir: *0.5m SW off B5106*
Built in the 17th century by Sir John Wynn
of Gwydir Castle, the chapel is noted for its
painted ceiling and wonderfully varied
woodwork.
Times: *Open any reasonable time.
Facilities: ℗ ⊗ ✛

TREFRIW
Trefriw Woollen Mills Ltd
Main Road, Conway Valley, LL27 0NQ
☎ 01492 640462
e-mail: info@t-w-m.co.uk
Web: www.t-w-m.co.uk
Dir: *on B5106 in centre of Trefriw, 5m N of
Betws-y-Coed*
Established in 1859, the mill is situated
beside the Afon Crafnant, which drives two
hydro-electric turbines to power the looms.
All the machinery of woollen manufacture can
be seen here. In the Weaver's Garden, there
are plants used in the textile industry, mainly
for dyeing. Hand-spinning demonstrations.
Times: Mill Museum open Etr-Oct, Mon-Fri
10-1 & 2-5. Weaving demonstrations &
turbine house: open all year, Mon-Fri 10-1 &
2-5. Handspinning & weaver's garden
Jun-Sep Tue-Thu, Jul-Aug Mon-Fri 10-5
Facilities: ℗ (35yds) ⊐ & (access to shop,
cafe, weaving & turbine house) shop
⊗ (ex assist dogs & on lead) 🚌 (must book)

EWLOE
Ewloe Castle
Web: www.cadw.wales.gov.uk
Dir: *1m NW of village on B5125*

Standing in Ewloe Wood are the remains of Ewloe Castle. It was a native Welsh castle, and Henry II was defeated nearby in 1157. Part of the Welsh Tower in the upper ward still stands to its original height, and there is a well in the lower ward. Remnants of walls and another tower can also be seen.

Times: *Open at all times.
Facilities: ⊗ ➡ ⊕

FLINT
Flint Castle
CH6 5PH
☎ 01352 733078
Web: www.cadw.wales.gov.uk
Dir: *NE side of Flint*

The castle was started by Edward I in 1277 and overlooks the River Dee. It is exceptional for its great tower, or Donjon, which is separated by a moat. Other buildings would have stood in the inner bailey, of which parts of the walls and corner towers remain.

Times: *Open at all times.
Facilities: ℗ ⊗ ➡ ⊕

FLINTSHIRE

FLINTSHIRE/GWYNEDD

HOLYWELL
Basingwerk Abbey

Greenfield Valley Heritage Pk, Greenfield, CH8 7GH

☎ 01352 714172

Web: www.cadw.wales.gov.uk

Dir: *just S of A458*

The abbey was founded around 1131 by Ranulf de Gernon, Earl of Chester. The first stone church dates from the beginning of the 13th century. The last abbot surrendered the house to the crown in 1536. The Abbey is close to the Heritage Park Visitor Centre and access to the Museum and Farm Complex at Greenfield Valley.

Times: *Open all year, daily 9-6.

Facilities: ❷ ⭑⭑ ⛩ ♿ (disabled facilities in Heritage Park), toilets for disabled, shop ⊗ 🚌 ✛

CAERNARFON
Segontium Roman Museum

Beddgelert Road, LL55 2LN

☎ 01286 675625

🖹 01286 678416

e-mail: info@segontium.org.uk

Web: www.segontium.org.uk

Dir: *on A4085 to Beddgelert approx 1m from Caernarfon*

Segontium Roman Museum tells the story of the conquest and occupation of Wales by the Romans and displays the finds from the auxiliary fort of Segontium, one of the most famous in Britain. You can combine a visit to the museum with exploration of the site of the Roman Fort, which is in the care of Cadw: Welsh Historic Monuments. The exciting discoveries displayed at the museum vividly portray the daily life of the soldiers stationed in this remote outpost of the Roman Empire.

Times: *Open all year Tue-Sun 12.30-4. Closed Mon except BH

Facilities: ℗ ⊗ (ex assist dogs) 🚌 (pre-booking preferred)

CYMER ABBEY
Cymer Abbey

☎ 01341 422854

Web: www.cadw.wales.gov.uk

Dir: *2m NW of Dolgellau on A494*

The abbey was built for the Cistercians in the 13th century. It was never very large, and does not seem to have been finished. The church is the best-preserved building, with ranges of windows and arcades still to be seen. The other buildings have been plundered for stone, but low outlines remain.

Times: *Open all year, early Apr-Oct, daily 9.30-6; Nov-Mar, daily 9.30-4. Closed 24-26 Dec & 1 Jan

Facilities: ⓟ ♿ ⊗ 🚌 ⊕

LLANBERIS
Dolbadarn Castle

LL55 4UD

Web: www.cadw.wales.gov.uk

Dir: *A4086*

Built by Llywelyn the Great in the early 13th century, this Welsh castle overlooks Llyn Padarn in the Llanberis Pass.

Times: *Open any reasonable time.

Facilities: ⓟ ⊗ 🚌 ⊕

GWYNEDD

GWYNEDD

LLANBERIS
Welsh Slate Museum

Gilfach Ddu, Padarn Country Park, LL55 4TY

☎ 01286 870630

🖷 01286 871906

e-mail: slate@museumwales.ac.uk

Web: www.museumwales.ac.uk

Dir: *0.25m off A4086. Museum within Padarn Country Park*

Set among the towering quarries at Llanberis, the Welsh Slate Museum is a living, working site located in the original workshops of Dinorwig Quarry, which once employed 15,000 men and boys. You can see the foundry, smithy, workshops and mess room which make up the old quarry, and view original machinery, much of which is still in working order.

Times: *Open Etr-Oct, daily 10-5; Nov-Etr, Sun-Fri 10-4.

Facilities: ❷ (charged) ☐ ☵ ♿ (all parts accessible except patten loft) toilets for disabled, shop ⊗ (ex assist dogs) 🚌 (pre-booking advisable)

LLANFIHANGEL-Y-PENNANT
Castell-y-Bere

☎ 029 2050 0200

Web: www.cadw.wales.gov.uk

Dir: *off B4405*

The castle was begun around 1221 by Prince Llewelyn ap Iorwerth of Gwynedd to guard the southern flank of his principality. It is typically Welsh in design with its D-shaped towers. Although a little off the beaten track, the castle lies in a spectacular setting, overshadowed by the Cader Idris range.

Times: *Open all reasonable times.

Facilities: ⊗ 🚌 ✛

LLANGYBI

St Cybi's Well

☎ 01766 810047

Web: www.cadw.wales.gov.uk

Dir: *off B4354*

Cybi was a 6th-century Cornish saint, known as a healer of the sick, and St Cybi's Well (or Ffynnon Gybi) has been famous for its curative properties through the centuries. The corbelled beehive vaulting inside the roofless stone structure is Irish in style and unique in Wales.

Times: *Open at all times.

Facilities: ♿ ⊗ 🚌 ⊕

PENARTH FAWR

Penarth Fawr

☎ 01766 810880

Web: www.cadw.wales.gov.uk

Dir: *3.5m NE of Pwllheli off A497*

The hall, buttery and screen are preserved in this house which was probably built in the 15th century.

Times: *Open at all times.

Facilities: ♿ ⊗ 🚌 ⊕

GWYNEDD

ISLE OF ANGLESEY

BRYNCELLI DDU
Bryn Celli Ddu Burial Chamber
☎ 029 2050 0200
Web: www.cadw.wales.gov.uk
Dir: *3m W of Menai Bridge off A4080*
Excavated in 1865, and then again in 1925-9, this is a prehistoric circular cairn covering a passage grave with a polygonal chamber.
Times: *Open at all times.
Facilities: ❷ ⊗ 🚌 ⚕

HOLYHEAD
RSPB Nature Reserve South Stack Cliffs
Plas Nico, South Stack, LL65 1YH
☎ 01407 764973
🖷 01407 764973
Web: www.rspb.org.uk/reserves/southstack
Dir: *A5 or A55 to Holyhead then follow brown heritage signs*
South Stack Cliffs is an expanse of heathland with dramatic sea cliffs and a tremendous view. In summer breeding seabirds, including puffins, can be seen from the Information Centre at Ellins Tower where telescopes are provided and staff are on hand to help.
Times: *Open: Information Centre daily, Etr-Sep, 10-5.30. Reserve open daily at all times.
Facilities: ❷ ♿ toilets for disabled, tours available 🚌 (pre-booking required)

LLANALLGO
Din Llugwy Ancient Village

Web: www.cadw.wales.gov.uk

Dir: *0.75m NW off A5025*

The remains of a 4th-century village can be seen here. There are two circular and seven rectangular buildings, still standing up to head height and encircled by a pentagonal stone wall some 4 to 5ft thick.

Times: *Open at all times.

Facilities: ⊗ 🚌 ⊕

MERTHYR TYDFIL
Cyfarthfa Castle Museum & Art Gallery

Cyfarthfa Park, CF47 8RE

☎ 01685 723112

🖷 01685 723112

e-mail: museum@merthyr.gov.uk

Web: www.museums.merthyr.gov.uk

Dir: *off A470, N towards Brecon, follow brown heritage signs*

Set in wooded parkland beside a lake, this imposing Gothic mansion houses a superb museum and art gallery. Providing a glimpse into 3,000 years of history, the museum displays collections of fine art, social history and objects from around the world.

Times: Open Apr-Sep, daily, 10-5.30; Oct-Mar, Tue-Fri 10-4, Sat-Sun 12-4. Closed between Xmas & New Year

Facilities: ❷ (restricted during some special events) ⊐ 🎠 ♿ (stair lift & wheel-chair available), toilets for disabled, shop, tours available ⊗ (ex assist dogs) 🚌 (pre-booking required)

MONMOUTHSHIRE

CAERWENT
Caerwent Roman Town
☎ 029 2050 0200
Web: www.cadw.wales.gov.uk
Dir: *just off A48*

A complete circuit of the town wall of 'Venta Silurum', together with excavated areas of houses, shops and a temple.

Times: Open - access throughout the year.
Facilities: ⊗ 🚌 ✛

GROSMONT
Grosmont Castle
☎ 01981 240301
Web: www.cadw.wales.gov.uk
Dir: *on B4347*

Grosmont is one of the 'trilateral' castles of Hubert de Burgh. It stands on a mound with a dry moat, and the considerable remains of its 13th-century great hall can be seen. Three towers once guarded the curtain wall, and the western one is well preserved.

Times: *Open - access throughout the year.
Facilities: ♿ ⊗ 🚌 ✛

LLANTHONY
Llanthony Priory

☎ 029 2050 0200

Web: www.cadw.wales.gov.uk

William de Lacey discovered the remains of a hermitage dedicated to St David. By 1108 a church had been consecrated on the site and just over a decade later the priory was complete. After the priory was brought to a state of siege in an uprising, Hugh de Lacey provided the funds for a new church, and it is this that makes the picturesque ruin seen today. Visitors can still make out the west towers, north nave arcade and south transept.

Times: *Open - access throughout the year.

Facilities: 🅿 ♿ ground floor only access, toilets for disabled 🚫 🚐 ⊕

LLANTILIO CROSSENNY
Hen Gwrt

☎ 029 2050 0200

Web: www.cadw.wales.gov.uk

Dir: *off B4233*

The rectangular enclosure of the former medieval house, still surrounded by a moat.

Times: *Open - access throughout the year.

Facilities: 🚫 ⊕

MONMOUTHSHIRE

MONMOUTHSHIRE

MONMOUTH
The Nelson Museum & Local History Centre

New Market Hall, Priory Street, NP25 3XA

☎ 01600 710630

e-mail: nelsonmuseum@monmouthshire.gov.uk

Dir: *in town centre*

One of the world's major collections of Admiral Nelson-related items, including letters, glass, china, silver, medals, books, models, prints and Nelson's fighting sword feature here. The local history displays deal with Monmouth's past as a fortress market town, and include a section on the co-founder of the Rolls Royce company, Charles Stewart Rolls, who was also a pioneer balloonist, aviator and, of course, motorist.

Times: Open all year, Mar-Oct, Mon-Sat, 11-1, 2-5, Sun, 2-5, including BHs. Nov-Feb, Mon-Sat, 11-2, 2-4, Sun, 2-4.

Facilities: ℗ (200yds) (small daily charge) ♿ toilets for disabled, shop ⊗ (ex assist dogs) 🚌 (pre-booking necessary)

SKENFRITH
Skenfrith Castle

☎ 029 2050 0200

Web: www.cadw.wales.gov.uk

Dir: *on B4521*

This 13th-century castle has a round keep set inside an imposing towered curtain wall. Hubert de Burgh built it as one of three 'trilateral' castles to defend the Welsh Marches.

Times: *Open - access throughout the year. Key keeper arrangement.

Facilities: ℗ ⊗ 🚌 ✛ 🐾

CRYNANT
Cefn Coed Colliery Museum
SA10 8SN

☎ 01639 750556

🖹 01639 750556

Dir: *1m S of Crynant, on A4109*

The museum is on the site of a former working colliery, and tells the story of mining in the Dulais Valley. A steam-winding engine has been kept and is now operated by electricity, and there is also a simulated underground mining gallery, boilerhouse, compressor house, and exhibition area. Outdoor exhibits include a stationary colliery locomotive. Exhibitions relating to the coal mining industry are held on a regular basis.

Times: *Open Apr-Oct,daily 10.30-5; Nov-Mar, groups welcome by prior arrangement.

Facilities: ❷ ⴲ toilets for disabled, shop, tours available 🚌

NEATH
Neath Abbey
SA10 7DW

☎ 01639 812387

Web: www.cadw.wales.gov.uk

Dir: *1m W off A465*

These ruins were originally a Cistercian abbey founded in 1130 by Richard de Grainville.

Times: *Open at all times. Key keeper arrangement.

Facilities: ❷ ⴲ ⊗ 🚌 ✛

NEATH PORT TALBOT

NEWPORT/PEMBROKESHIRE

CAERLEON
National Roman Legion Museum
High Street, NP18 1AE
☎ 01633 423134
🖷 01633 422869
e-mail: roman@museumwales.ac.uk
Web: www.museumwales.ac.uk
Dir: *close to Newport, 20 min from M4,
follow signs from Cardiff & Bristol*

The museum illustrates the history of Roman
Caerleon and the daily life of its garrison. On
display are arms, armour and equipment, with
a collection of engraved gemstones, a
labyrinth mosaic and finds from the legionary
base at Usk. Please telephone for details of
children's holiday activities.

Times: *Open all year: Mon-Sat 10-5,
Sun 2-5.

Facilities: ℗ (100yds) ♿ toilets for disabled
shop ⊗ (ex assist dogs) 🚌 (advance booking essential)

LLAWHADEN
Llawhaden Castle
☎ 01437 541201
Web: www.cadw.wales.gov.uk
Dir: *off A40, 3m NW of Narberth*

The castle was first built in the 12th century to
protect the possessions of the Bishops of St
David's. The 13th and 14th-century remains
of the bishops' hall, kitchen, bakehouse and
other buildings can be seen, all surrounded
by a deep moat.

Times: *Open at all times. Key keeper
arrangement.

Facilities: ♿ ⊗ 🚌 ⊕

NEWPORT
Pentre Ifan Burial Chamber
☎ 029 2050 0200
Web: www.cadw.wales.gov.uk
Dir: *3m SE from B4329 or A487*

Found to be part of a vanished long barrow when excavated in 1936-37, the remains of this chamber include the capstone, three uprights and a circular forecourt.

Times: *Open - access throughout the year.
Facilities: ⊗ 🚌 ♿

MONTGOMERY
Montgomery Castle
☎ 029 2050 0200
Web: www.cadw.wales.gov.uk

Initially an earth and timber structure guarding an important ford in the River Severn, Montgomery was considered a 'suitable spot for the erection of an impregnable castle' in the 1220s. Building and modifications continued until 1251-53, but the final conquest of Wales by Edward I meant the castle lost much of its role.

Times: *Open all year, any reasonable time.
Facilities: ♿ ⊗ 🚌 ♿

PEMBROKESHIRE/POWYS

SWANSEA/TORFAEN

SWANSEA

Swansea Museum

Victoria Road, Maritime Quarter, SA1 1SN

☎ 01792 653763

🖹 01792 652585

e-mail: swansea.museum@swansea.gov.uk

Web: www.swanseaheritage.co.uk

Dir: *M4 junct 42, on main road into city centre*

This is the oldest museum in Wales, showing the history of Swansea from the earliest times until today. The museum has a Tramshed and floating boats to explore (summer only). There is a continuous programme of temporary exhibitions and events all year around.

Times: *Open all year, Tue-Sun 10-5 (last admission 4.45). Closed Mon except BH Mon, 25-26 Dec & 1 Jan.

Facilities: ℗ (50yds) (on street) ♿ toilets for disabled, shop ⊗ (ex assist dogs) 🚌 (prior notification preferred)

BLAENAVON

Big Pit National Mining Museum of Wales

Torfaen, NP4 9XP

☎ 01495 790311

🖹 01495 792618

e-mail: bigpit@nmgw.ac.uk

Web: www.nmgw.ac.uk/bigpit

Dir: *M4 junct 25/26, follow signs on A4042 & A4043 to Pontypool & Blaenavon. Signed off A465*

The Real Underground Experience! Big Pit is the UK's leading mining museum. It is a real colliery and was the place of work for hundreds of men, woman and children for over 200 years. A daily struggle to extract the precious mineral that stoked furnaces and lit household fires across the world.

Times: *Open mid Feb-late Nov, daily 9.30-5, telephone to confirm

Facilities: ℗ ⊑ (licensed) ♿ (underground tours by prior arrangement), toilets for disabled, shop 🚌 (pre-booking required)

OGMORE

Ogmore Castle

☎ 01656 653435

Web: www.cadw.wales.gov.uk

Dir: *2.5m SW of Bridgend, on B4524*

Standing on the River Ogmore, the west wall of this castle is 40ft high. A hooded fireplace is preserved in the 12th-century, three-storey keep and a dry moat surrounds the inner ward.

Times: *Open - access throughout the year. Key keeper arrangement.

Facilities: Ⓟ ♿ ⊗ 🚌 ⊕

ST HILARY

Old Beaupre Castle

☎ 01446 773034

Web: www.cadw.wales.gov.uk

Dir: *1m SW, off A48*

This ruined manor house was rebuilt during the 16th century. Its most notable features are an Italianate gatehouse and porch. The porch is an unusual three-storeyed structure.

Times: *Open - access throughout the year. Key keeper arrangement.

Facilities: Ⓟ ⊗ 🚌 ⊕ 🌳

VALE OF GLAMORGAN

BELFAST

BELFAST
Botanic Gardens

3 College Park, Off Botanic Ave., BT7 1LP

☎ 028 9032 4902

🖹 028 9032 4902

e-mail: maxwellr@belfastcity.gov.uk

Web: www.belfastcity.gov.uk

Dir: *from City Hall, Bedford St then Dublin road for Botanic Avenue*

One highlight of the park is the beautiful glass-domed Victorian Palm House, built between 1839-52. This palm house pre-dates the one in Kew Gardens and is one of the earliest curved glass and iron structures in the world. Another feature is the Tropical Ravine - stand on a balcony to get a wonderful view through a steamy ravine full of exotic plants.

Times: *Open Palm House Tropical Ravine: Apr-Sep 10-12, 1-5; Oct-Mar 10-12, 1-4. Sat, Sun & BHs 1-5 (Summer), 1-4 (Winter).

Facilities: ℗ (street) ♿ toilets for disabled, accessed by radar key, tours available 🚌

BELFAST
Giant's Ring

☎ 028 9023 5000

🖹 028 9031 0288

Web: www.ehsni.gov.uk

Dir: *0.75m S of Shaws Bridge*

Circular, Bronze-age enclosure nearly 200ft in diameter similar in style to Stonehenge, with a stone chambered grave in the centre and bordered by banks 20ft wide and 12ft high. Very little is known for certain about this site, except that it was used for ritual burial.

Times: *Open all times.

Facilities: ℗

BELFAST
Ulster Museum

National Museums of N.Ireland, Botanic Gardens, BT9 5AB

☎ 028 9038 3000

🖺 028 9038 3003

e-mail: info@magni.org.uk

Web: www.ulstermuseum.org.uk

Dir: *1m S of city centre on Stranmillis road*

Explore the arts, ancient and modern history, and the nature of Ireland. Art displays always include a rich variety of Irish and international paintings, drawings and sculpture, along with ceramics, glass and costume. The History galleries tell the story of the north of Ireland from Ice Age to present day. Explore the natural environment in the Habitas galleries.

Times: *Open all year, Mon-Fri 10-5, Sat 1-5, Sun 2-5. Closed 3 days Xmas

Facilities: Ⓟ (100yds on street) 🆒 ⅃ (lifts, loop system) toilets for disabled (adapted toilet on ground floor), shop, audio commentaries available ⊗ (ex assist dogs) 🚌 (pre-booking preferred)

ANTRIM
Antrim Round Tower

BT41 1BJ

☎ 028 9023 5000

🖺 028 9031 0288

Web: www.ehsni.gov.uk

Dir: *N of town*

Antrim round tower stands among lawns and trees but it was once surrounded by monastic buildings. Antrim was an important early monastery, probably a 6th-century foundation, closely linked with Bangor.

Times: *Open all year.

Facilities: Ⓟ ⅃

CO ANTRIM

BALLYCASTLE
Bonamargy Friary
☎ 028 9023 5000
🖺 028 9031 0288
Web: www.ehsni.gov.uk
Dir: *E of town, at golf course*
Founded by Rory MacQuillan around 1500 and later passed on to the MacDonnells, Earls of Antrim, there are still remains of the friary gatehouse, church and cloister for visitors to see.
Times: *Open all year.
Facilities: 🅿 ⅋

BALLYLUMFORD
Ballylumford Dolmen
☎ 028 9023 5000
🖺 028 9031 0288
Web: www.ehsni.gov.uk
Dir: *on B90 on NW tip of Island Magee*
Incorporated in the front garden of a house in Ballylumford Road are the remains of this huge 4-5,000-year-old single-chamber Neolithic tomb, also known as the Druid's Altar.
Times: *Open all year.
Facilities: ⅋

BALLYMENA

Ecos Millennium Environmental Centre

Ecos Centre, Kernohams Lane, Broughshane Road, BT43 7QA

☎ 028 2566 4400

🖹 028 2563 8984

e-mail: info@ecoscentre.com

Web: www.ecoscentre.com

Dir: *follow signs from M2 bypass at Ballymena*

A fun day out on the Ecos Island with a wide range of fun activities, including electric bikes, remote control boats, toy tractors and diggers sand pit, BBQ's and picnicking facilities. Information on the environment and renewable energy technologies. Set in a 150-acre park and nature reserve where visitors can follow walking trails along the riverside.

Times: *Open all year. Please phone for opening dates. Closed 24 Dec-1 Jan

Facilities: ❷ ⛄ 🎋 ♿ toilets for disabled, shop, garden centre, audio commentaries available ⊗ (ex assist dogs) 🚌

BALLYMENA

Harryville Motte

☎ 028 9023 5000

🖹 028 9031 0288

Web: www.ehsni.gov.uk

Dir: *N bank of River Braid*

On a ridge to the south of the town, this Norman fort, with its 40ft-high motte and rectangular bailey, is one of the finest examples of Norman earthworks left in Northern Ireland.

Times: *Open all year.

Facilities: ❷ ♿

CO ANTRIM

CO ANTRIM

CARRICKFERGUS
Town Walls
☎ 028 9023 5000
▤ 028 9031 0288
Web: www.ehsni.gov.uk

Lord Deputy Sir Arthur Chichester enclosed Carrickfergus with stone walls from 1611 onwards and more than half the circuit is still visible, often to its full height of 4 metres to the wall walk.

Times: *Visible at all times.
Facilities: ℗ (charge under consideration) ♿ 🚌

CHURCHTOWN
Cranfield Church
☎ 028 9023 5000
▤ 028 9031 0288
Web: www.ehsni.gov.uk
Dir: *3.75m SW of Randalstown*

This small medieval church is situated on the shores of Lough Neagh. Beside it is a famous holy well.

Times: *Open all year.
Facilities: ℗ ⛱ ♿

LARNE
Olderfleet Castle

☎ 028 9023 5000

🖶 028 9031 0288

Web: www.ehsni.gov.uk

A 16th-century tower house, the last surviving of three which defended Larne.

Times: *Open at all times.

Facilities: 🚌

LISBURN
Duneight Motte and Bailey

☎ 028 9023 5000

🖶 028 9031 0288

Web: www.ehsni.gov.uk

Dir: *2.3m S beside Ravernet River*

Impressive Anglo-Norman earthwork castle with high mound-embanked enclosure, making use of the defences of an earlier pre-Norman fort.

Times: *Open all year.

Facilities: 🚌

CO ANTRIM

LISBURN
Irish Linen Centre & Lisburn Museum

Market Square, BT28 1AG

☎ 028 9266 3377

🖷 028 9267 2624

e-mail: irishlinencentre@lisburn.gov.uk

Web: www.lisburncity.gov.uk

Dir: *Signed both in and outside town centre. Follow tourist signs from M1*

The centre tells the story of the Irish linen industry past and present. The recreation of individual factory scenes brings the past to life and a series of imaginative hands-on activities describe the linen manufacturing processes. The Museum has a range of temporary exhibitions of local interest.

Times: Open all year, Mon-Sat, 9.30-5.

Facilities: ℗ (100yds) (limited for disabled and coaches) ⊵ (licensed) ໕ (lift, induction loop, staff trained in sign language), toilets for disabled, shop, tours ⊗ (ex assist dogs) 🚌 (advance booking preferred)

TEMPLEPATRICK
Templetown Mausoleum

BT39

Web: www.ntni.org.uk

Dir: *in Castle Upton graveyard on A6, Belfast-Antrim road*

Situated in the graveyard of Castle Upton, this family mausoleum is in the shape of a triumphal arch and was designed by Robert Adam.

Times: *Open daily during daylight hours.

Facilities: ❷ ℗ 200 yds ♨

ARMAGH
Armagh County Museum

The Mall East, BT61 9BE

☎ 028 3752 3070

🖹 028 3752 2631

e-mail: acm.um@nics.gov.uk

Web: www.magni.org.uk

Dir: *in city centre*

Housed in a 19th-century schoolhouse, this museum contains an art gallery and library, as well as a collection of local folkcrafts and natural history. Special events are planned thoughout the year.

Times: *Open all year, Mon-Fri 10-5, Sat 10-1 & 2-5.

Facilities: 𝐏 ℗ (500yds) ♿ (entrance, ramp & lift for disabled), toilets for disabled (on ground floor, alarmed, hand rails), shop ⊗ (ex assist dogs) 🚌

ARMAGH
Armagh Friary

☎ 028 9023 5000

🖹 028 9031 0288

Web: www.ehsni.gov.uk

Dir: *SE edge of town*

Situated just inside the gates of the former Archbishop's Palace are the remains of the longest friary church in Ireland (163ft). The friary was established in 1263 by Archbishop O'Scanail and destroyed by Shane O'Neill in the middle of the 16th century to prevent it being garrisoned by Elizabethan soldiers.

Times: *Open all year.

Facilities: 𝐏 ♿ 🚌

CO ARMAGH

CO ARMAGH

CAMLOUGH
Killevy Churches
☎ 028 9023 5000

🖷 028 9031 0288

Web: www.ehsni.gov.uk

Dir: *3m S lower eastern slopes of Slieve Gullion*

The ruins of the two churches (10th and 13th-century) stand back to back, at the foot of Slieve Gullion sharing a common wall, but with no way through from one to the other. The churches stand on the site of an important nunnery founded by St Monenna in the 5th century. A huge granite slab in the graveyard supposedly marks the founder's grave. A holy well can be reached by climbing the path north of the graveyard. The nunnery was in use until the Dissolution in 1542.

Times: *Open all year.

Facilities: ⅗ 🚌

JONESBOROUGH
Kilnasaggart Inscribed Stone
☎ 028 9023 5000

🖷 028 9031 0288

Web: www.ehsni.gov.uk

Dir: *1.25m S*

A granite pillar stone dating back to 8th century, with numerous crosses and a long Irish inscription carved on it.

Times: *Open all year.

Facilities: ℗

NEWRY
Moyry Castle

☎ 028 9023 5000

📄 028 9031 0288

Web: www.ehsni.gov.uk

Dir: *7.5m S*

This tall, three-storey keep was built by Lord Mountjoy, Queen Elizabeth's deputy, in 1601, its purpose to secure the Gap of the North which was the main route into Ulster.

Times: *Open all year

Facilities: 🚌

TYNAN
Village Cross

☎ 028 9023 5000

📄 028 9031 0288

Web: www.ehsni.gov.uk

A carved High Cross, 11ft tall, which lay broken in two pieces for many years, but was skilfully mended in 1844.

Times: *Open all year

Facilities: 🅿 ♿ all parts accessible 🚌

CO ARMAGH

CO DOWN

ARDGLASS
Jordan's Castle
☎ 028 9054 6552

Web: www.ehsni.gov.uk

Although Ardglass is an important fishing port today, it was once the busiest seaport in Northern Ireland. Between the 14th and 15th centuries a ring of tower houses and fortified warehouses was built to protect the port. Jordan's Castle, a late 15th-century, four-storey tower house situated in the centre of town, is one of these. Besieged in the early 1600s and held for three years, the castle was bought, repaired and filled with bygones by a Belfast solicitor in the early part of the 20th century.

Times: *Open Jul-Aug; Tue, Fri & Sat 10-1, Wed-Thu, 2-6. Other times on request.

Facilities: toilets for disabled ⊗ 🚌

BALLYWALTER
Grey Abbey
☎ 028 9054 6552

Web: www.ehsni.gov.uk

Dir: *on E edge of village*

Founded in 1193 by Affreca, daughter of the King of the Isle of Man, these extensive ruins of a Cistercian abbey, sitting in sheltered parkland, are among the best preserved in Northern Ireland. The chancel, with its tall lancet windows, magnificent west doorway and an effigy tomb - believed to be Affreca's - in the north wall, are particularly interesting. The abbey was burned down in 1572, and then re-used as a parish church. There are many 17th and 18th-century memorials to be seen in the church ruins, which occupy a pleasant garden setting. The abbey now has a beautiful medieval herb garden, with over 50 varieties of plants, and a visitors' centre.

Times: *Open Apr-Sep; Tue-Sat 10-7, Sun 2-7; Oct-Mar, wknds, Sat 10-4, Sun 2-4.

Facilities: 🅿 ♿ toilets for disabled 🚌

CASTLEWELLAN

Drumena Cashel

☎ 028 9023 5000

🖹 028 9031 0288

Web: www.ehsni.gov.uk

Dir: *2.25m SW*

There are many stone ring forts in Northern Ireland, but few so well preserved as Drumena. Dating back to early Christian times, the fort is 30mtr in diameter and has an 11mtr accessible underground stone-built passage, probably used as a refuge and for storage.

Times: *Open all times

Facilities: ℗ 🚌

DOWNPATRICK

Down County Museum

The Mall, BT30 6AH

☎ 028 4461 5218

🖹 028 4461 5590

e-mail: museum@downdc.gov.uk

Web: www.downcountymuseum.com

Dir: *on entry to town follow brown signs*

The museum is located in the restored buildings of the 18th-century county gaol. In addition to restored cells that tell the stories of some of the prisoners, there are exhibitions on the history of County Down. Plus exhibits, events, tea-room and shop.

Times: Open all year, Mon-Fri 10-5, wknds 1-5

Facilities: ℗ (100yds) ⌷ 🍴 ♿ (wheelchair available, handling boxes on application), toilets for disabled (located in cell block) shop, tours available, audio commentaries available ⊗ (ex assist dogs) 🚌 (advance booking for guided tours)

CO DOWN

CO DOWN

DOWNPATRICK

Loughinisland Churches

☎ 028 9023 5000

🖷 028 9031 0288

Web: www.ehsni.gov.uk

Dir: *4m W*

This remarkable group of three ancient churches stands on an island in the lough, accessible by a causeway. The middle church is the oldest, probably dating back to the 13th century, with a draw-bar hole to secure the door. The large North church was built in the 15th century, possibly to replace the middle church and continued in use until 1720. The smallest and most recent church is the South (MacCartan's) church.

Times: *Open all times

Facilities: ❷ ♿ all parts accessible

DOWNPATRICK

Mound of Down

☎ 028 9023 5000

🖷 028 9031 0288

Web: www.ehsni.gov.uk

Dir: *on Quoile Marshes, from Mount Crescent*

A hill fort from the Early Christian period, conquered by Anglo-Norman troops in 1177, who then built an earthwork castle on top. This mound in the marshes, beside the River Quoile, was the first town before the present Downpatrick.

Times: *Open all times

Facilities: ❷ 🚌

DOWNPATRICK
Struell Wells

☎ 028 9023 5000

🖹 028 9031 0288

Web: www.ehsni.gov.uk

Dir: *1.5m E*

Pilgrims come to collect the healing waters from these holy drinking and eye wells which are fed by a swift underground stream. Nearby are the ruins of an 18th-century church, and, even more interesting, single-sex bath-houses. The men's bath-house is roofed, has an anteroom and a sunken bath, while the ladies' is smaller and roofless.

Times: *Open all times

Facilities: ℗

DROMARA
Legananny Dolmen

☎ 028 9023 5000

🖹 028 9031 0288

Web: www.ehsni.gov.uk

Dir: *4m S*

Theatrically situated on the slopes of Slieve Croob, this tripod dolmen with its three tall uprights and huge capstone is the most graceful of Northern Ireland's Stone Age monuments. There are views to the Mourne Mountains.

Times: *Open at all times

Facilities: ♿ all parts accessible

CO DOWN

CO DOWN

HILLSBOROUGH
Hillsborough Fort

☎ 028 9268 3285

🖹 028 9031 0288

Web: www.ehsni.gov.uk

On a site that dates back to early Christian times, the existing fort was built in 1650 by Colonel Arthur Hill to command a view of the road from Dublin to Carrickfergus. The building was ornamented in the 18th century. It is set in a forest park with a lake and pleasant walks.

Times: *Open all year; Apr-Sep, Tue-Sat 10-7, Sun 2-7; Oct-Mar, Tue-Fri 10-4, Sat 10-4, Sun 2-4

Facilities: ℗ ㈗ ♿

KILLINCHY
Sketrick Castle

☎ 028 9023 5000

🖹 028 9031 0288

Web: www.ehsni.gov.uk

Dir: *3m E on W tip of Sketrick Islands*

A badly ruined tall tower house, probably 15th century. The ground floor rooms include a boat bay and prison. An underground passage leads from the north-east of the bawn to a freshwater spring.

Times: *Open at all times.

Facilities: ℗ ㈗ ♿ 🚌

NEWCASTLE
Dundrum Castle

☎ 028 9054 6518

Web: www.ehsni.gov.uk

Dir: *4m N*

This medieval castle, one of the finest in Ireland, was built in 1777 by John De Courcy in a strategic position overlooking Dundrum Bay, a position which offers visitors fine views over the sea and to the Mourne Mountains. The castle was captured by King John in 1210 and was badly damaged by Cromwellian troops in 1652. Still an impressive ruin, it shows a massive round keep with walls 16 metres high and 2 metres thick, surrounded by a curtain wall, and a gatehouse which dates from the 13th century.

Times: *Open Apr-Sep, Tue-Sat 10-7, Sun 2-7; Oct-Mar, wknds, Sat 10-4, Sun 2-4.

Facilities: ❷ 🅟 ♿ toilets for disabled 🚐

NEWCASTLE
Maghera Church

☎ 028 9023 5000

🖷 028 9031 0288

Web: www.ehsni.gov.uk

Dir: *2m NNW*

The stump of a round tower, blown down in a storm in the early 18th century, survives from the early monastery, with a ruined 13th-century church nearby.

Times: *Open all year.

Facilities: ❷ ♿ 🚐

CO DOWN

CO DOWN

NEWTOWNARDS
Scrabo Tower

Scrabo Country Park, 203A Scrabo Road, BT23 4SJ

☎ 028 9181 1491

🖹 028 9182 0695

Web: www.ehsni.gov.uk

Dir: *1m W*

The 135ft high Scrabo Tower, one of Northern Ireland's best-known landmarks, dominates the landscape of North Down and is also the centre of a country park around the slopes of Scrabo Hill. The Tower provides fascinating interpretative displays about the surrounding countryside and the viewing platform boasts spectacular views over Strangford Lough and Co. Down. The park provides walks through fine woodlands and the sandstone quarries display evidence of volcanic activity as well as being breeding sites for peregrine falcons.

Times: *Open late Mar-mid Sep, Sat-Thu 10.30-6.

Facilities: ❷ ㅠ toilets for disabled, shop ⊗ 🚌

STRANGFORD
Audley's Castle

☎ 028 9023 0560

🖹 028 9031 0288

Web: www.ehsni.gov.uk

Dir: *1.5m W by shore of Strangford Lough*

15th-century tower house on Strangford Lough which offers lovely views from its top floor. The internal fittings are complete.

Times: *Open Apr-Sep, daily 10-7.

Facilities: ❷ ⊗ 🚌

STRANGFORD
Strangford Castle

☎ 028 9023 5000

🖹 028 9031 0288

Web: www.ehsni.gov.uk

A three-storey tower house built in the 16th century, overlooking the small double harbour of Strangford.

Times: *Open all reasonable times.

Facilities: 🚫 🚐

DERRYGONNELLY
Tully Castle

☎ 028 9054 6552

Web: www.ehsni.gov.uk

Dir: *3m N, on W shore of Lower Lough Erne*

Extensive ruins of a Scottish-style strong-house with enclosing bawn overlooking Lough Erne. Built by Sir John Hume in the early 1600s, the castle was destroyed, and most of the occupants slaughtered, by the Maguires in the 1641 Rising. There is a replica of a 17th-century garden in the bawn.

Times: *Open Jul & Aug, Wed-Sun, 10-6.

Facilities: 🅿 🚻 ♿ 🚫 🚐

CO DOWN/CO FERMANAGH

CO FERMANAGH

ENNISKILLEN
Monea Castle

☎ 028 9023 5000

🖷 028 9031 0288

Web: www.ehsni.gov.uk

Dir: *6m NW*

A fine example of a plantation castle still with much of its enclosing bawn wall intact, built around 1618. Of particular interest is the castle's stone corbelling - the Scottish method of giving additional support to turrets.

Times: *Open at any reasonable time.

Facilities: ℗ ⅊ 🚐

LISNASKEA
Castle Balfour

☎ 028 9023 5000

🖷 028 9031 0288

Web: www.ehsni.gov.uk

Dating from 1618 and refortified in 1652, this is a T-plan house with vaulted rooms. Badly burnt in the early 1800s, this house has remained in ruins.

Times: *Open at all times.

Facilities: ℗ ⅊ 🚐

COLERAINE
Mount Sandel
☎ 028 9023 0560
▤ 028 9031 0288
Web: www.ehsni.gov.uk
Dir: *1.25m SSE*

This 200ft oval mound overlooking the River Bann is believed to have been fortified in the Iron Age. Nearby is the earliest known inhabited place in Ireland, where post holes and hearths of wooden dwellings, and flint implements dating back to 6,650BC have been found. The fort was a stronghold of de Courcy in the late 12th century and was refortified for artillery in the 17th century.

Times: *Open at all times.
Facilities: ⊘ ♿ 🚌

DUNGIVEN
Banagher Church
☎ 028 9023 5000
▤ 028 9031 0288
Web: www.ehsni.gov.uk
Dir: *2m SW*

This church was founded by St Muiredach O'Heney in 1100 and altered in later centuries. Today impressive ruins remain. The nave is the oldest part and the square-headed lintelled west door is particularly impressive. Just outside, the perfect miniature stone house, complete with pitched roof and the sculpted figures of a saint at the doorway, is believed to be the tomb of St Muiredach. The saint was said to have endowed his large family with the power of bringing good luck. All they had to do was to sprinkle whoever or whatever needed luck with sand taken from the base of the saint's tomb.

Times: *Open at all times.
Facilities: ⊘ ♿ 🚌

CO LONDONDERRY

CO LONDONDERRY

DUNGIVEN
Dungiven Priory
☎ 028 9023 5000
🖹 028 9031 0288
Web: www.ehsni.gov.uk
Dir: *SE of town overlooking River Roe*

Up until the 17th century Dungiven was the stronghold of the O'Cahan chiefs, and the Augustinian priory, of which extensive ruins remain, was founded by the O'Cahans around 1150. The church, which was altered many times in later centuries, contains one of Northern Ireland's finest medieval tombs. It is the tomb of Cooey na Gall O'Cahan who died in 1385. His sculpted effigy, dressed in Irish armour, lies under a stonework canopy. Below are six kilted warriors.

Times: *Open Church at all times, chancel only when caretaker available. Check at house at end of lane.
Facilities: 🅿 ♿ 🚌

LIMAVADY
Rough Fort
☎ 028 7084 8728
🖹 028 7084 8728
e-mail: downhillcastle@nationaltrust.org.uk
Web: www.ntni.org.uk
Dir: *1m W off A2*

Early Christian rath picturesquely surrounded by pine and beech trees, making it a significant landscape feature. The Rough Fort is one of the best examples of an earthwork ring fort in Ireland.

Times: *Open at all times.
Facilities: 🐾

MAGHERA
Maghera Church

☎ 028 9023 5000

▤ 028 9031 0288

Web: www.ehsni.gov.uk

Dir: *E approach to the town*

Important 6th-century monastery founded by St Lurach, later a bishop's see and finally a parish church. This much-altered church has a magnificently decorated 12th-century west door. A cross-carved stone to the west of the church is supposed to be the grave of the founder.

Times: *Key from Leisure Centre.

Facilities: ❷ ♿ 🚌

ARDBOE
Ardboe Cross

☎ 028 9023 5000

▤ 028 9031 0288

Web: www.ehsni.gov.uk

Dir: *off B73*

Situated at Ardboe Point, on the western shore of Lough Neagh, is the best example of a high cross to be found in Northern Ireland. Marking the site of an ancient monastery, the cross has 22 sculpted panels, many recognisably biblical, including Adam and Eve and the Last Judgment. It stands over 18ft high and dates back to the 10th century. It is still the rallying place of the annual Lammas, but praying at the cross and washing in the lake has been replaced by traditional music-making, singing and selling of local produce. The tradition of 'cross reading' or interpreting the pictures on the cross, is an honour passed from generation to generation among the men of the village.

Times: *Open at all times.

Facilities: ❷ ♿ 🚌

CO TYRONE

BEAGHMORE
Beaghmore Stone Circles and Alignments

☎ 028 9023 5000

🖶 028 9031 0288

Web: www.ehsni.gov.uk

Discovered in the 1930s, these impressive, ritualistic stones have been dated back to the early Bronze, and maybe even Neolithic Ages. There are three pairs of stone circles, one single circle, stone rows or alignments and cairns, which range in height from one to four feet. This is an area littered with historic monuments, many discovered by people cutting turf.

Times: *Open at all times.

Facilities: 🅿 ♿

BENBURB
Benburb Castle

☎ 028 9023 5000

🖶 028 9031 0288

Web: www.ehsni.gov.uk

The castle ruins - three towers and massive walls - are dramatically placed on a cliff-edge 120ft above the River Blackwater. The north-west tower is now restored and has dizzy cliff-edge views. The castle, built by Sir Richard Wingfield around 1615, is actually situated in the grounds of the Servite Priory. There are attractive walks down to the river.

Times: *Castle grounds open at all times. Special arrangements, made in advance, necessary for access to flanker tower.

Facilities: 🅿 ♿ ⊗ 🚌

CASTLECAULFIELD

Castle Caulfield

☎ 028 9023 5000

🖹 028 9031 0288

Web: www.ehsni.gov.uk

Sir Toby Caulfield, an Oxfordshire knight and ancestor of the Earls of Charlemont, built this manor house in 1619 on the site of an ancient fort. It was badly burnt in 1641, repaired and lived in by the Caulfield/Charlemont family until 1670. It boasts the rare distinction of having had Saint Oliver Plunkett and John Wesley preach in its grounds. Some fragments of the castle are re-used in the fine, large 17th-century parish church.

Times: *Open at all times.

Facilities: ℗ & 🚌

COOKSTOWN

Tullaghoge Fort

☎ 028 9023 5000

🖹 028 9031 0288

Web: www.ehsni.gov.uk

Dir: *2m S*

This large hilltop earthwork, planted with trees, was once the headquarters of the O'Hagans, Chief Justices of the old kingdom of Tyrone. Between the 12th and 16th centuries the O'Neill Chiefs of Ulster were also crowned here - the King Elect was seated on a stone inauguration chair, new sandals were placed on his feet and he was then anointed and crowned. The last such ceremony was held here in the 1590s; in 1600 the stone throne was destroyed by order of Lord Mountjoy.

Times: *Open at all times.

Facilities: ℗ 🚌

CO TYRONE

CO TYRONE

MOUNTJOY
Mountjoy Castle

Magheralamfield, Stewartstown

☎ 028 9023 5000

🖹 028 9031 0288

Web: www.ehsni.gov.uk

Dir: *3m SE, off B161*

Ruins of an early 17th-century brick and stone fort, with four rectangular towers, overlooking Lough Neagh. The fort was built for Lord Deputy Mountjoy during his campaign against Hugh O'Neill, Earl of Tyrone. It was captured and re-captured by the Irish and English during the 17th century and was also used by the armies of James II and William III.

Times: *Open at all times.

Facilities: 🅿 🚌

NEWTOWNSTEWART
Harry Avery's Castle

☎ 028 9023 5000

🖹 028 9031 0288

Web: www.ehsni.gov.uk

Dir: *0.75m SW*

The hilltop ruins of a Gaelic stone castle, built around the 14th century by one of the O'Neill chiefs, are the remains of the oldest surviving Irish-built castle in the north. Only the great twin towers of the gatehouse are left. A stairway enables the public to gain access to one of these.

Times: *Open at all times.

Facilities: ⊗

CARRIGTWOHILL
Fota Arboretum & Gardens

Fota Estate

☎ 021 4812728

🖹 021 4812728

e-mail: info@heritageireland.ie

Web: www.heritageireland.ie

Dir: *14km from Cork on Cobh road*

Fota Arboretum contains an extensive collection of trees and shrubs extending over an area of approx 27 acres and includes features such as an ornamental pond and Italian walled gardens. The collection includes many tender plants that could not be grown at inland locations, with many examples of exotic plants from the Southern Hemisphere.

Times: *Arboretum: Open Apr-Oct, Mon-Sat 9-6, Sun 11-6; Nov-Mar, Mon-Sat 9-5, Sun 11-5. Walled Gardens: Apr-Oct, Mon-Fri. Selected Sun openings please ring for times and dates.

Facilities: ❷ (charged) ⋒ ♿ toilets for disabled 🚌

BALLYSHANNON
The Water Wheels

Abbey Assaroe

☎ 071 9851580

Dir: *cross Abbey River on Rossnowlagh Rd, next turning left & follow signs*

Abbey Assaroe was founded by Cistercian Monks from Boyle Abbey in the late 12th century, who excelled in water engineering and canalised the river to turn water wheels for mechanical power. Two restored 12th-century mills, one is used as coffee shop and restaurant; the other houses a small museum related to the history of the Cistercians. Interesting walks in the vicinity.

Times: Open May-Oct, daily 10.30-6.30

Facilities: ❷ ☕ ⅋◯⅃ (licensed) ⋒ ♿ toilets for disabled, shop, garden centre 🚌 (40/50 people)

DUBLIN
The Chester Beatty Library

The Clock Tower Building, Dublin Castle

☎ 01 4070750

🖷 01 4070760

e-mail: info@cbl.ie

Web: www.cbl.ie

Dir: *10 mins walk from Trinity College, up Dame St towards Christ Church Cathedral*

The contents of this fascinating gallery was bequeathed to Ireland by its first honorary citizen, American mining engineer/collector, Sir Alfred Chester Beatty (1875-1968). The collection includes manuscripts, prints, icons, miniatures, and important objects from 2700BC to the present day. See illuminated copies of the Qur'an and the Bible, Egyptian papyrus texts, and Buddhist paintings.

Times: *Open all year, May-Sep, Mon-Fri 10-5; Oct-Apr, Tue-Fri 10-5, Sat 11-5, Sun 1-5. Closed BHs.

Facilities: ℗ (5 mins walk) ☐ ⑩ ♿ toilets for disabled, shop ⊗ (ex assist dogs) 🚌 (must contact in advance)

DUBLIN
National Photographic Archive

Meeting House Square, Temple Bar

☎ 01 6030200

🖷 01 6777451

e-mail: photoarchive@nli.ie

Web: www.nli.ie

Dir: *opposite The Gallery of Photography*

The National Photographic Archive, which is part of the National Library of Ireland, was opened in 1998 in an award-winning building. The archive holds an unrivalled collection of photographic images relating to Irish history, topography and cultural and social life. The collection is rich in late 19th and early 20th century topographical views and studio portraits. Includes photographs taken during the Rebellion of 1916 and the subsequent War of Independence and Civil War.

Times: *Open all year, Mon-Fri 10-5. (Closed BHs, Good Fri & 23 Dec-2 Jan).

Facilities: ♿ toilets for disabled, shop ⊗ (ex assist dogs) 🚌 (prior notice required)

DUBLIN
National Library of Ireland
Kildare Street
☎ 01 6030200
🖷 01 6766690

Web: www.nli.ie

Founded in 1877 and based on collections from The Royal Dublin Society. The National Library holds an estimated 5 million items. There are collections of printed books, manuscripts, prints and drawings, photos, maps, newspapers, microfilms and ephemera. The library's research facilities are open to all those with genuine research needs. In addition to research facilities, services include a regular programme of exhibitions open to the public and Genealogy Service.

Times: *Open all year, Mon-Wed 10-9, Thu-Fri 10-5 & Sat 10-1. Closed Sun, BHs, Good Fri & 23 Dec-2 Jan.

Facilities: ♿ toilets for disabled, shop ⊗ (ex assist dogs)

DUBLIN
Howth Castle Rhododendron Gardens
Howth
☎ 01 8322624 & 8322256
🖷 01 8392405

e-mail: sales@deerpark.iol.ie

Dir: *9m NE of city centre, by coast road to Howth. Before Howth follow signs for Deer Park Hotel*

Overlooking the sea on the north side of Dublin Bay, the rhododendron walks command spectacular views of the Castle and Ireland's Eye. The flowers are at their best in May and June. Visitors should be aware that the gardens are in some disrepair and the paths somewhat rough and overgrown in parts.

Times: *Open all year, daily 8am-dusk. Closed 25 Dec.

Facilities: 🅿 ♿ (steep hills unsuitable, ramped entrance) toilets for disabled ⊗ (ex assist dogs) 🚌

CO DUBLIN

CO DUBLIN

DUBLIN
Dublin City Gallery The Hugh Lane
Charlemont House, Parnell Square

☎ 01 2222550

▤ 01 8722182

e-mail: info@hughlane.ie

Web: www.hughlane.ie

Dir: *Off O'Connell St Parnell Monument. At the top of Parnell Square*

Situated in Charlemont House, a fine Georgian building, the gallery has one of the most extensive collections of 20th-century Irish art, international and Irish paintings, sculpture, works on paper and stained glass, plus a reconstruction of Francis Bacon's Studio. Lectures and concerts on Sundays.

Times: *Open all year, Tue-Thu 10-6, Fri-Sat 10-5, Sun 11-5. Closed Mon, Good Fri & 24-25 Dec.

Facilities: Ⓟ (100yds) (meter parking) ☑ (licensed) ♿ (ramp & reserved parking), toilets for disabled, shop, tours available, audio commentaries available ⊗ (ex assist dogs) 🚐

DUBLIN
National Botanic Gardens
Glasnevin

☎ 01 8374388 & 8377596

▤ 01 8360080

Dir: *on Botanic Road, between N1 and N2*

Ireland's premier Botanic Gardens, covers a total area of 19.5 hectares (48 acres), part of which is the natural flood plain of the River Tolka. The Gardens contain a large plant collection, which includes approximately 20,000 species and cultivated varieties. There are four ranges of glasshouses including the restored Curvilinear Range.

Times: *Open all year, Gardens: Summer Mon-Sat 9-6, Sun 11-6; Winter Mon-Sat 10-4.30, Sun 11-4.30. (Closed 25 Dec). Glasshouses: Summer Mon-Wed & Fri 9-5, Thu 9-3.15, Sat 9-5.45, Sun 2-5.45; Winter, Mon-Wed, Fri & Sat 10-4.15, Thu 10-3.15, Sun 2-4.15.

Facilities: Ⓟ (charged) ☑ ♿ toilets for disabled ⊗ (ex assist dogs)

DUBLIN
Irish Museum of Modern Art

Royal Hospital, Military Road, Kilmainham

☎ 01 6129900

🖷 01 6129999

e-mail: info@imma.ie

Web: www.imma.ie

Dir: *3.5km from city centre, just off N7 opposite Heuston Station*

Housed in the Royal Hospital Kilmainham, an impressive 17th-century building, the Irish Museum of Modern Art is Ireland's leading national institution for the collection and presentation of modern and contemporary art. It presents a variety of art and artists' ideas in a programme of exhibitions, which regularly includes work from the museum's collection.

Times: *Open all year, Tue-Sat 10-5.30, Sun & BHs 12-5.30. Closed Mon & 24-26 Dec.

Facilities: ❷ ☗ (licensed) ♿ toilets for disabled, shop ⊗ (ex assist dogs) ▦

DUBLIN
Natural History Museum

Merrion Street

☎ 01 6777444

🖷 01 6777828

e-mail: education.nmi@indigo.ie

Dir: *in city centre*

The Natural History Museum, which is part of The National Museum of Ireland, is a zoological museum containing diverse collections of world wildlife. The Irish Room, on the ground floor, is devoted largely to Irish mammals, sea creatures and insects. It includes the extinct giant Irish deer and the skeleton of a basking shark. The World Collection, has as its centre piece, the skeleton of a 60-ft whale suspended from the roof. Other displays include the Giant Panda and a Pygmy Hippopotamus.

Times: *Open all year, Tue-Sat 10-5, Sun 2-5. Closed Mon, 25 Dec & Good Fri

Facilities: ℗ (parking meters weekdays) ⊗ ▦

CO DUBLIN

SKERRIES
Skerries Mills

☎ 01 8495208

🖹 01 8495213

e-mail: skerriesmills@indigo.ie

Dir: *signed off M1*

A collection of restored mills, including a watermill, a five-sail, and a four-sail windmill, all in working order. The site dates from the 16th century and was originally part of a monastic establishment. It came into private ownership in 1538, and a bakery has been there since 1840. Nature lovers will enjoy the millpond, nearby wetlands and town park, of which the mills are the focal landmark.

Times: *Open all year Apr-Sep, daily 10.30-5.30; 2 Jan-Mar & Oct-19 Dec, daily 10.30-4.30. Closed Good Fri

Facilities: ❷ ⬚ ⬚ (licensed), toilets for disabled, shop, tours available ⊗ 🚌

GALWAY
Royal Tara China Gift Centre

Tara Hall, Mervue

☎ 091 705602

🖹 091 757574

e-mail: mkilroy@royal-tara.com

Web: www.royal-tara.com

Dir: *N6 from Tourist Office. At rdbt take 2nd left & at lights turn right*

Royal Tara China visitor centre, located minutes from Galway City Centre, operates from a 17th-century house situated on five acres.

Times: *Open all year, Mon-Sat 9-5, Sun 10-5

Facilities: ❷ ♿ (all facilities accessible for disabled) toilets for disabled fully fitted, shop ⊗ (ex assist dogs) 🚌 (pre-book only)

ROUNDSTONE

Roundstone Music, Crafts & Fashion

Craft Centre

☎ 095 35875

🖷 095 35980

e-mail: bodhran@iol.ie

Web: www.bodhran.com

Dir: *N59 from Galway to Clifden. After approx 50m turn left at Roundstone sign, 7m to village. Attraction at top of village*

The Roundstone Music Craft and Fashion shop is located within the walls of an old Franciscan Monastery. Here you can see Ireland's oldest craft: the Bodhran being made. Talks and demonstrations. The 1st RiverDance stage drums were made here and are on display in the Craftsman's Craftshop. Picnic area by the water where dolphins swim.

Times: Open Apr-Oct 9.30-6, Jul-Sep 9-7, Winter 6 days 9.30-6.

Facilities: ♿ 🍽 (licensed) 🎪 ♿ toilets for disabled (handrails, ramps) shop, tours available ⊗ (ex assist dogs) 🚌

KEENAGH

Corlea Trackway Visitor Centre

☎ 043 22386

🖷 043 22442

e-mail: ctrackwayvisitorcentre@opw.ie

Dir: *off R397, 3km from village, 15km from Longford*

The centre interprets an Iron Age bog road which was built in the year 148BC across the boglands close to the River Shannon. The oak road is the largest of its kind to have been uncovered in Europe and was excavated over the years by Professor Barry Raferty of University College Dublin. Inside the building, an 18-metre stretch of preserved road is on permanent display in a specially designed hall with humidifiers to prevent the ancient wood from cracking in the heat.

Times: *Open Apr-Sep, daily 10-6

Facilities: ♿ 🍽 🎪 ♿ toilets for disabled ⊗ (ex assist dogs) 🚌

CO MONAGHAN/CO WEXFORD

MONAGHAN

Monaghan County Museum

1-2 Hill Street

☎ 047 82928

🖹 047 71189

e-mail: comuseum@monghancoco.ie

Web: www.monaghan.ie

Dir: *near town centre, opposite market house exhibition galleries*

This is an award-winning museum of local archaeology, history, arts and crafts. Throughout the year various special exhibitions take place.

Times: *Open Sep-May, Tue-Fri 10-1 & 2-5 Sat 11-1 & 2-5. Jun-Aug, Mon-Fri 11-5, Thu 11-7, Sat 11-1 & 2-5.

Facilities: Ⓟ (near town centre) (restricted on-street parking) ♿ ⊗ (ex assist dogs) 🚌 (pre-booking required)

WEXFORD

Wexford Wildfowl Reserve

North Slob

☎ 053 23129

🖹 053 24785

e-mail: info@heritageireland.ie

Dir: *8km NE from Wexford*

The reserve is of international importance for Greenland white-fronted geese, Brent geese, Bewick's swans and wigeon. The reserve is a superb place for birdwatching and there are hides and a tower hide available as well as a visitor centre.

Times: *Open all year daily, 9-5. Other hours by arrangement with the warden. Closed 25 Dec. Reserve may be closed temporarily for management operations - Notice on gate.

Facilities: Ⓟ 🅿 ♿ toilets for disabled, tours available ⊗ (ex assist dogs) 🚌 (pre-booking essential)